# ANATOMY OF AN EXPEDITION

# Anatomy of an Expedition

**HENRY W. MENARD**

Institute of Marine Resources
and
Scripps Institution of Oceanography
University of California, San Diego

**McGraw-Hill Book Company**

New York    St. Louis    San Francisco    London    Sydney    Toronto    Mexico    Panama

**ANATOMY OF AN EXPEDITION**

**ACKNOWLEDGMENTS**

Photographs used in the insert section were taken by C. E. Abranson
and Alan Jones, as well as by the
author.
Pen-and-ink drawings were taken
from the following books by Sir C.
Wyville Thompson: "Report on the
Scientific Results of the Voyage of
H.M.S. Challenger," Her Majesty's
Stationery Office, London, Narrative,
vol. I, pts. 1 and 2 (1885), and Narrative, vol. II (1882); "The Voyage of
the Challenger," MacMillan and Company, London, 1877, vols. I and II.

To Robert Dietz and Roger Revelle, coleaders of the joint U.S. Navy-Scripps Institution of Oceanography Expedition *Mid-Pac* which, in 1950, took many young oceanographers into the deep sea for the first time.

# *Preface*

During the last two decades the deep sea floor—two-thirds of the world—has been explored for the first time. For a hundred years a few scientists had known it as a dark, cold, and utterly alien world. Now it is becoming familiar to schoolchildren who have maps of the sea floor next to the maps of the moon on their classroom walls. How did this come about? A small group of deep sea oceanographers of all nations simply went out into the ocean basins again and again and discovered the mountains, the trenches, the volcanoes, and the rifts one by one. The exploration began near the great scientific ship bases: Woods Hole, Vladivostok, Palisades, Plymouth, La Jolla, Sevastopol. Then it spread through the Atlantic and Pacific and finally the Indian Oceans, and now it goes round and round the world. I believe that it is realistic to say that the geographical discoveries have been on a scale unmatched since the sixteenth century, when the continents were disclosed to Western eyes.

I wonder if any of the people involved have thought of the oceanic exploration of the last two decades in any such grand terms? I doubt it very much; they have been and continue to be too busy. This book is an attempt to show some of the things that keep oceanographers busy, how at a certain place and time a group of them went to sea and why. All expeditions are different, but I think that *Nova* is a fair sample of the hundreds that have plied the oceans in recent years. Thus this record of improvisations, misadventures, and adjustments may have some merit in being an honest account of typical events written as they occurred.

The oceanographer leads a curious life of contrasts. He sticks close to his desk but takes it out to sea from time to time. At sea, the oceanographer is in the same role as a chemist in a laboratory; he is trying to find facts that test ideas or that may lead to new hypotheses. The level of science may not be very high until the ships return to land and data have been analyzed and digested. Moreover, all scientists who work in the natural environment—geologists, oceanographers, meteorologists, zoologists—have to do partially uncontrolled experiments. Those concerned with the earth sciences have the further complication that they are dealing not only with vast areas but also with an enormous span of time. Thus it is something of an achievement merely to establish a definite relationship or sequence of events. For these reasons the practitioners of the exact sciences will see litttle science and a lot of sailing and fact-finding in the latter chapters of this book. Perhaps it would be fair to compare this account of the *Nova* Expedition to a naval operation report. The first few chapters of the report give the strategic situation and operation plan, and the latter chapters the diary and summary of tactical operations. Integration of the results into some broader synthesis requires contemplation and time which is not available during operations at sea.

This book may seem to have little to say directly about oceanographers on the *Nova* Expedition, but, without invading their privacy, it can be taken for granted that they are the kinds of people who do the kinds of things described. They are also people with an irresistible necessity to go aroving and have adventures and who are lucky enough to make a living at it. If there are any readers who share these tastes, now is the time to plunge in. The scientific exploration and the search for the wealth of the sea have just begun. In terms of the earlier phase of global exploration, the *Nova* Expedition was in the year 1493.

**Henry W. Menard**

# Contents

# ANATOMY OF AN EXPEDITION

# *Genesis of an Expedition*

**CHAPTER ONE**  An oceanographic expedition is the crystallization of an idea; it begins and ends in the mind with a little sailing around in between. The idea that became the *Nova* Expedition began to take form in the fall of 1965. At that time, I had not been to sea for fourteen months, which was my longest period on land since I became an oceanographer in 1949, and I started to think about another expedition. It is now March 1967 and the expedition is about to begin, and at this point I cannot remember exactly when or where the subject first came under discussion. After fifteen expeditions the preliminaries get rather vague. Most expeditions, and I suppose this was no exception, are conceived late in the evening after enough oceanographers have become sufficiently relaxed to be optimistic about work at sea. The reason for this is that everyone knows that the eventual output is going to require a lot of hard labor and discomfort. The conversation can be generalized as follows:

"Ed, why don't we go drill an atoll and find out why it sank?"

"Say that's great. I need a sequence of reef limestones to test this new idea...."

"Which atoll? What about Fakarava?"

"Where's Fakarava?"

"You remember. Where we stopped on the *Downwind* Expedition in the central Tuamotus."

"Yeah, that was nice, and we can get fuel and plane service at Tahiti. When?"

"Well, there is a gap in the ship schedule for *Argo* next July because Sam canceled out. He can't get delivery on his equipment. We could take some students along."

"I was going to visit Cambridge that month on my way back from the meeting in Stockholm, but I could go there before the meeting."

"We'll need to know the crustal structure in order to pick the best spot to drill. I wonder if George would be interested. Where is George? Hey, George how would you like to go to Fakarava next July?"

Perhaps one out of five of these evening expeditions eventually puts to sea, and then it is at Majuro because the Navy will provide free air service and in August because the ship needs an overhaul in July.

Considering that it is the taxpayer's money, it may sound a little casual, but oceanographers constantly get new ideas to test, and they have to go to sea at one time or another, and there is no virtue in going to an unpleasant atoll if a beautiful one has the same geology. In any event, there is stringent product control. If you don't produce results, you can't get money for your next expedition. You may not get the results you expected—this is research, not bridge building—but you have to get significant results of some sort.

An expedition needs an idea, scientists who are interested in it, a ship capable of the work, and money. Bringing them together takes a lot of talking, adjustment, writing, modification, time, flexibility, and work. The steps have not changed in the last 150 years. The first United States Exploring Expedition in 1838 and the first great oceanographic expedition on the *Challenger* in 1873 followed the same path of organization as the *Nova* Expedition in 1967. Indeed, these and the intervening expeditions had similar problems, used about the same size ships, and cost similar amounts. The great changes have been in the ideas under investigation and the equipment on the ships. All this historical precedent, however, is little consolation as the painful process is repeated yet again.

The basic idea of *Nova* is to try to determine the development and geological history of the peculiar Melanesian region in the southwestern Pacific where the sea floor seems to be part continent and part ocean basin. I shall elaborate on this shortly. Because the region is on the opposite side of the Pacific from Scripps Institution of Oceanography, the ships will incidently be available for other work coming and going. Several scientists at Scripps were immediately interested in the idea, and we decided to try to get a commitment for some time on one or more of our oceanographic ships. The ships belong to Scripps, and a committee of our oceanographers schedules their use. Even so, ships are hard to come by because so many scientists want them. On my first inquiry in the fall of 1965, I found that the next long period definitely available on one of our ships was in August of 1968, and then only if I had any plans for the area between Mauritius and Cape Town in the Indian Ocean. Fortunately some of my interested colleagues had time allotted in 1967, and by juggling the schedule with other scientists we put several months of ship time into one continuous block and still had everyone as happy as before. The next step was to look for money.

It may be useful at this point to consider how oceanographic expeditions are financed and what they cost. Captain Cook's first voyage in 1768–1770 was supported by King George III with a grant plus a bark, *Endeavour*. The total cost for the ship and outfitting exceeded £8235, and it appears that the voyage cost at least £10,000 or in round terms about $28,000. This sounds very modest, but for comparison with modern expeditions we must allow for the decreasing value of money. At that time, for example, a man with an income of $1200 a year was able to "keep five or six servants indoors and out, to look well after his relations, to travel freely, and to exercise a generous hospitality to rich and poor."

A reasonable approach is to assume that the purchasing power of a given amount of money has decreased by two percent per year. Accordingly, it takes seven times as much money to buy something at the end of a century as it does at the start. Consequently, it cost King George about 1,400,000 modern dollars for Cook's voyage. In addition, the scientist, Banks, whose tax-free income in modern terms was about $1,000,000 per year, put in a considerable amount of his own money. The expedition lasted almost three years and in modern money cost a minimum of $1300 per day.

The cost of the first United States Exploring Expedition (Wilkes Expedition) in 1838–1842 is buried beyond recall in government records. However, in 1836 Congress appropriated $300,000 for the expedition, and the Navy reported that it was all spent in 1837, a year before the ships put to sea. The expedition involved four ships for four years and cost perhaps $10,000,000 in modern money. Each ship cost more than $2000 per day even though all were very small and some did not last for four years. A century and a quarter later, during *Nova*, we expect to land on the Exploring Islands, named after and surveyed by this expedition.

The value of the *Challenger* Expedition of 1873–1876 was enormous and so was its cost. The British government apparently paid out a sum equivalent to the estimated expense for the recent Mohole Project to drill a hole in the bottom of the sea. The modern project would have been so expensive that the American Congress in 1966 decided that the richest country in the history of the world could not afford it.

So, on historical precedent we needed to locate some rich and generous patrons if the *Nova* Expedition were ever going to sea. Fortunately for the success of American oceanography some far-sighted men established just such funding organizations fifteen to twenty years ago. No longer must appeals for support for each expedition be directed to king or Congress. Indeed, it would be quite impossible to have 50 to 100 American oceanographic expeditions per year without the existence and support of federal agencies. The most important for the past two decades has been the Office of Naval Research, which produced modern oceanography by supporting the expansion of marine institutions and fleets of research vessels. Somewhat later the National Science Foundation entered the picture and now provides about half the support.

The main cost of oceanography is for ship time. A research ship without support for operating funds is an albatross around the neck of an oceanographic institution. Not too long ago the cost of a ship had to be justified on the scientific merits of each expedition. Consequently, oceanographic institutions were in about the position of a business which rents out ships but cannot make a profit to cover the expenses while the ship is idle. The daily cost of a ship was determined at the end of a year by dividing the annual cost by the number of days of use. It was a gigantic gamble to use an unpopular ship for a week at the start of the fiscal year. An oceanographer might find that he was expected to find funds for fifty-one idle weeks. This insane system seemed necessary because of the federal system of appropriating money for only one year. Finally, a few years ago officials in the Navy and the National Science Foundation figured out how to fund ships on an annual basis, and life became much simpler.

The total cost of *Nova* was initially estimated as follows:

| | |
|---|---:|
| ARGO, ship time at $3000/day | $ 720,000 |
| HORIZON, ship time at $2500/day | 400,000 |
| Direct support of expedition | 270,000 |
| Indirect costs of research | 100,000 |
| Scientific and technical salaries | 200,000 |
| | $1,690,000 |

This is certainly a staggering amount, but at $4000 per day per ship it is roughly what king or Parliament or Congress has always paid for marine expeditions during the last 200 years. It would have been much cheaper not too long ago. On our first Scripps deep sea expedition in 1950, *Horizon* cost only $450 per day, but that was before we loaded it with special equipment.

Due to the recent advances in federal money handling we did not need to ask for money to support the ships (which includes wages for the crew). Moreover, most of the salaries for scientists and technicians are paid by the University of California or by long-term state and federal research contracts. The indirect costs of research are those connected with this expedition but which are paid out of existing contracts with some broad objective. Thus the National Science Foundation supports a global study of carbon dioxide in the atmosphere, and some of this money will be used to make measurements during this particular expedition. In sum, in order to put this costly enterprise under way, we estimated that we needed $270,000, or about 15 percent of the total.

My colleagues, Harmon Craig, Edward Goldberg, Edward Winterer, Robert Fisher, and Manuel Bass, plus Charles Helsley of the Graduate Center of the Southwest, joined me in submitting a request to the National Science Foundation for this amount on 13 May 1966. As in all such proposals, we said what we want to do and why it is worth doing, who we are,

**The general plan of** *Nova*.

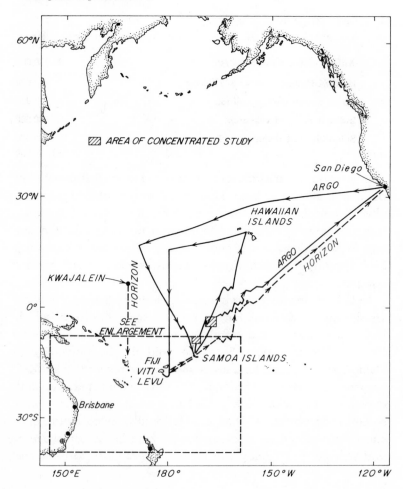

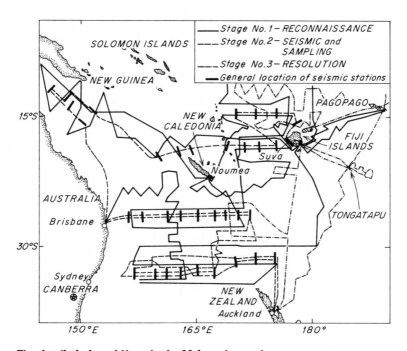

The detailed plan of *Nova* in the Melanesian region.

what we have done that makes it likely that we can do what we are asking money to do, the capabilities of our university to carry out the proposed work, and what it will cost. This proposal went through the customary elaborate review. It was sent to scientists doing related work at other institutions, and they graded it according to the quality of the scientific proposal and the abilities of the people and university. Then a geophysical review panel of government and academic scientists compared our evaluated proposal with those from other scientists and universities and arranged them in order of merit with due consideration of the cost. It is easy to identify one of these panel members if you ride on the airplane he is taking to a meeting. He has with him three brown-covered volumes of proposals with a total thickness of about eight inches, and he is busily reading the last one while other people watch the movie. He does this three times a year and thus evaluates about two feet of proposals requesting perhaps $20,000,000. It is hard work. I was on the panel for three years and for the same reason as the other members. I never met anyone who likes it, but we all agree that if scientists won't evaluate the merits of scientific proposals then it will have to be done by nonscientists who may have to judge proposals by criteria other than scientific merit.

This evaluation process takes three to six months, and meanwhile planning for an expedition has to continue with the hope that it will not be wasted. My colleagues and I talked to other scientists who might be interested in problems in the southwestern Pacific. Gradually more of them decided to participate in *Nova*, and technicians and special equipment were organized and integrated into as comprehensive and efficient a whole as possible. We did not need to know which ports we would use for fueling when we submitted the request for funds. However, we did need such information before sailing so we examined various permutations of ports, distances, ship speeds, fuel consumption, water supplies, explosive handling, airplane connections, and general logistics. Some matters require a long lead time. My hair is very short because when I was a poor graduate student my wife cut my hair and she liked it short. However, like all blonds, I have a skin sensitive to the sun and my hair is getting thin. I usually wear a hat in the tropics, but it seemed prudent to have some natural covering between the top of my head and the tropic sun. Consequently, seven months before the anticipated departure time I started to let my hair grow.

Early in August I got a phone call from Joe Creager, an oceanographer from the University of Washington who was doing his public service by working for a year with the National Science Foundation. He said that our proposal was approved on ·merit but that it cost more money than was available. Could we get along with less? I said we could, although with less I did not think that we could do everything we planned. How much less? Joe said "Half," and another time of troubles began.

What to cut? The categories in our proposal included salaries, assistantships for graduate students, supplies, equipment, travel, and a 42 percent markup to cover University overhead on salaries and wages. Almost all graduate students in oceanography receive substantial support, and most of it comes from federal contracts. This is not unreasonable, because the students help collect and analyze the results. On average they are the cheapest, highest-quality, and most eager workers in the world. We cut support for four students out of the budget, but we knew we would have to find the money somewhere else.

The next item was supplies and expenses. I quote from Sir Wyville Thomson concerning the outfitting of the *Challenger* Expedition in 1873:

> **It is almost inconceivable how difficult it is to keep instruments, particularly those which are necessarily made of steel, in working order on board a ship; or how rapidly even with the greatest care they become destroyed or lost. For this reason it is necessary to have an almost unlimited supply of those in most frequent use, such as scissors, forceps, and scalpels of all sizes.**

We have the same problems and must constantly restock everything from pencils to expendable equipment which is used only once but is cheaper than the ship time necessary to recover it. We chopped our request for supplies mercilessly but again with the certain knowledge that we would have to ask for more for the next expedition. We did have one windfall. George Shor, who had decided to measure crustal thickness in the southwestern Pacific, needed a large supply of explosives for the purpose. This was in the *Nova* budget, but meanwhile a long-standing request for explosives from the Navy was at last granted and we did not need more from the National Science Foundation. That item alone saved $12,000.

Next we came to heavier equipment which we also wear out or lose in the normal course of oceanographic work. We are not the only ones. A Russian oceanographer, Gleb Udintsev, once learned that we were planning to dredge in the world's deepest water in the Marianas Trench. He told me that if we dredged up a deep sea camera it was his because he had lost one there. The camera cost about $10,000 and we did not find it—in fact we lost one ourselves. What can you expect when you attach a camera to six miles of wire and try to photograph the rocky sea floor from a drifting ship? We eliminated the least urgent items and hoped for good fortune at sea and future replacements even though they would be of no use on this voyage.

Finally we came to a whopping request for $76,400 for travel by air to various ports that the ships would touch. We got our Marine Facilities department which operates the ships to agree to pay for rotating the crew, and that cut the request in half. Of course, it also increased the ship operating cost, but that was covered by another budget. We could have eliminated all this air travel by merely returning the ships to San Diego every few months, but that would have been a waste of money—which is a very different thing from tailoring requests for money to fit the amounts available in different contracts.

After many a painful session we cut the budget request in half and resubmitted the proposal on 10 August. Creager knew how short the planning time was growing and soon phoned that the money was on the way. He also said that he had hoped that we might reduce the amount of ship time required because the Science Foundation was running short of money for ships. After our juggling this seemed a little ironical.

One problem we face at Scripps is naming an expedition after we create it. This does not arise at every oceanographic institution nor was it ever necessary in the past. If the Royal Society sent the *Challenger* around the world, the voyage was called the "*Challenger* Expedition," which was entirely adequate because no expectation existed that the ship would ever go on another expedition. Likewise the "*Galathea* Expedition" and the "Swedish Deep-Sea Expedition" clearly were conceived as unique efforts. When such ships as *Atlantis* and the *E. W. Scripps* began to be used for repeated cruises in the 1930s, the problem of identifying the results arose and two solutions were used. A sample is uniquely designated by the ship name, cruise number, and sample number, thus: *Atlantis*, Cruise 6, Sample 4, or by specifying the cruise location, thus: *Scripps*, Gulf of California, Sample 4. However, the second system may produce confusion if the ship returns to the Gulf of California, and it is not very useful if the expedition is to a

nameless place such as the region where a certain ocean current exists, e.g., the Gulf Stream. Lamont Geological Observatory and the Russian Institute of Oceanology, among others,
give each cruise a number, but initially by chance and later
by design we name ours.

The first large Scripps expedition in the deep sea was
focused on the mountains of the central Pacific and was
named *Mid-Pac*. It was followed by *Northern Holiday*, which
derived its name from the nautical term "holiday," meaning a
place where no information exists. The name caused a little
muttering among the financing agencies in Washington. When
it was proposed that *Northern Holiday* be followed by *Southern
Holiday*, the muttering became audible in La Jolla. Warren
Wooster, who was in charge of the expeditions, decided the
Navy was not ready for nautical terminology and changed the
name. Then we had expeditions with a variety of names, such
as *Capricorn* after the Tropic of Capricorn, which was the
southern limit of the region explored, and *Cascadia*, which
was the name of a continent thought to have once existed off
Oregon where we were working. We had a great series of
wind names typical of the region of operations: *Chubasco,
Chinook, Zephyrus, Downwind, Monsoon*. We had momentary
aberrations like *Six-Pac* and inspirations like *Blue Flash*, which
was one of the first cruises using an arcer—which emits such
a flash. We began to have so many similar names such as
*Dolphin* and *Dorado* which means the same thing but in Spanish that we were in danger of confusing the samples. We all
agreed not to name an expedition without the prior approval
of Bill Riedel, curator of geological samples, who would en-
sure that the abbreviation of a suggested name would not be
the same as one already used.

What to name the new expedition to Melanesia? Usually
several weeks or even months pass before the natural name
of an expedition emerges. It becomes increasingly inconve-
nient to organize a nameless expedition or one which different
people call by different names. Finally Jerry Winterer noted
that the region we would study contained New Caledonia,
New Zealand, New Guinea, and the New Hebrides and suggested the name *Nova*. It was short, pertinent, and distinctive,

and Riedel was enthusiastic because we had few "N" expeditions. Now we had a name.

Next, or meanwhile, we needed to make base maps for our work. If you want a map to do something like hike in the Sierras or navigate a ship into Suva harbor you just buy one from the appropriate government agency. Not so in oceanography, where the maps have to be changed after each expedition and commonly are made on board in order to plan the next day's work. We needed to know about every unpublished geophysical observation anyone had taken in the southwestern Pacific, in order to avoid duplication and for making detailed plans. The only way to get such information is to write to or visit every person who might have it. There are both formal and informal worldwide information networks whereby oceanographers keep track of their colleagues' work. I had already acquired a large amount of information by making the usual carefully respected promises not to publish other people's unpublished data and by agreeing to make our own observations similarly available. There remained the problem of the most recent data collected by oceanographers in Australia, New Zealand, and New Caledonia. A lot is always known which has not even been processed to the point where it can be sent to anyone else. I needed that information but getting it would require work by other people whose time I did not want to waste. The only practical solution was to visit the laboratories and explain exactly what we hoped to do and what information we needed. The trip would also provide an opportunity to interest oceanographers in these countries in participating in *Nova* and thereby getting more scientific results from the same effort at sea. In any event, it is not very courteous to carry out a lengthy expedition in waters near other oceanographic laboratories without asking the scientists there if they would like to join in. Finally, the trip would give me a chance to inspect prospective ports once again and see whether the surrounding countryside would be suitable for geological field trips for the students.

My wife had never been in this region so we went through the necessary arrangements to leave our children. A month later we had talked to geologists and oceanographers and naval hydrographers in Wellington, Sydney, Noumea, and Suva; scanned the geology and logistic support available in the surrounding regions; given talks about the expedition plans and found a number of bright young oceanographers who wanted to participate; and had a load of unpublished charts and manuscripts and a painting of a mining scene by Pro Hart. We had had a delightful time thanks to the hospitality and generosity of many people we knew and others we had not met before. Many should reappear during the course of the expedition.

Back in La Jolla my associates Stuart Smith, Tom Chase, and Isabel Taylor plunged into the compilation of the new data for our base charts. Tom and Stu were each to lead one of the early legs of the expedition and had a vital need for this information. I also had the assistance of several graduate students who would join in the work at sea and might eventually use some of the results for Ph.D. theses.

My own effort was concentrated on further planning. The possible permutations in an enterprise like this are beyond belief. Somehow all the senior scientists have to be satisfied that their work can be done, equipment and supplies have to be directed to the right places at the right times, and the budget has to be balanced. It always reminds me of planning an amphibious assault—as I did in the same region many years ago—except that money is important.

I have mentioned the explosives before; the further problems connected with this item alone may illustrate something of what is involved. George Shor had about 12 tons of TNT stockpiled in the Navy ammunition depot in Pearl Harbor. Another similar amount would provide all we needed, and it was available in Southern California. However, *Horizon* could not carry its half of the explosives because its magazine had to take supplies needed for other work before we took it over in Kwajalein in April, 1967. It could have returned to Pearl Harbor, but that would have reduced time in the southwestern Pacific. We hit upon an elaborate scheme. *Argo* was scheduled to conduct oceanographic work from San Diego to Pago Pago to Pearl Harbor and then back south to Suva, where it would be joined by *Horizon*. We could load the local TNT on

*Argo*, unload and store it at Pago Pago, and then reload the ship with the Pearl Harbor TNT when it reached there. *Horizon*, which by then would be half empty, would make a short trip to Pago Pago and back to Suva collecting useful although less important data on the way. But could we store explosives at Pago Pago? Appropriate inquiries indicated that we could. Could both ships enter Suva harbor with explosives? We knew from previous expeditions that we had done so, but had the port regulations changed? Our ship agent in Suva said that they had and we would have to unload everything onto a barge in midstream before coming to the dock for fuel. So a little time might be lost.

At about this time a new development entered the explosives problem. Charles Helsley, of the Graduate Center of the Southwest, would also measure crustal thickness and structure on *Nova*. He flew to La Jolla, and he and George Shor developed some intricate negotiations whereby the TNT in California became an equal quantity of Nitramon, which is commercial fertilizer except when it is triggered by an explosive fuse. This safe stuff could be stored on *Argo* outside the magazine and would not have to be off-loaded at Pago Pago before the magazine was filled with TNT at Pearl Harbor. Consequently, *Horizon* need not go to Pago Pago and would be available for more important work. Moreover, Helsley would shoot off all the TNT between Suva and Brisbane, and we should have no problem entering the latter port, which had not yet replied to our inquiries about bringing in explosives. Then Brisbane said it would not let us enter even with the quantity of explosive fuses needed to set off the Nitramon.

So why were we going to Brisbane? Originally we planned to stop at that time in Noumea because it is more centrally located in the southwestern Pacific and it costs less to fly there from California than to Brisbane. However, Helsley had to ship some of his gear on to South Africa to join another oceanographic expedition. To meet this other sailing date he had to have the gear in a port with frequent sailings instead of Noumea, and so we put all other considerations aside. With the news from Brisbane about explosives, the port question was raised again. It turned out that a ship sails on an irregular schedule from Noumea to Sydney about the time we should arrive. By radioing from sea for a final sailing date we could be sure to arrive in time to load Helsley's gear. I phoned him in Texas to ask if this port change was agreeable to him considering the new information about freighter sailings. He agreed and said, moreover, the expedition off Africa was now looking questionable and he was no longer in such a hurry about sending his equipment there. We decided to stop at Noumea, where explosives are brought in frequently for the mines.

The above is a simplified version of the explosives problem. Helsley also shipped some Nitramon from Texas which was supposed to go by commercial truck. A trucking strike stopped that. The Nitramon came by truck driven by a graduate student and his wife. The truck broke down but was repaired and arrived just before sailing time.

There were also the mysterious and complicated affairs of the different air fares to Pago Pago, the missing magnetometers, the carbon dioxide program, and the perplexing problem of who would be working in the Coral Sea.

Finally, in April 1967, *Horizon* sailed south from Kwajalein and *Argo* sailed west from San Diego. The *Nova* Expedition was under way, seventeen months after it was conceived. Not a bad record, really; the *Challenger* Expedition took eighteen months and the United States Exploring Expedition took more than ten years to do the same thing.

fall 1965-march 1967
CHAPTER TWO

# Exploration of
# the Pacific Basin

**CHAPTER TWO**    Before we follow our ships on *Nova*, I would like to describe something of what was known about the Pacific when they sailed. Books on the exploration of the Pacific are numerous indeed but are generally biased in emphasizing the role of European explorers in the sixteenth through nineteenth centuries. This attitude is very hard to reconcile with the simple facts, namely, a few thousand square miles of Pacific islands were found by the Polynesians and Micronesians; the islanders were found by the European "explorers"; and everything else in the Pacific basin has been found by oceanographers during the last hundred years. I shall attempt to put these matters in perspective, although it would hardly be surprising if this account is also biased by my own experiences.

With regard to the Polynesians, I follow the lucid account of Andrew Sharp. It appears that from the time of Christ to that of Magellan, various peoples originating in southeast Asia spread across the Pacific. They sailed across the open ocean sometimes by design but often by chance until the whole region from Asia to Easter Island was occupied. At least once, perhaps more frequently, they visited South America and brought back the sweet potato and a few other things. When Quiros discovered the island of Hao in the Tuamotus in 1606, he found a woman who had a gold ring with an emerald. And where do emeralds come from if not Peru?

Blown about by storms, taking advantage of unusual winds, daring the endless sea, the Polynesians occupied the Pacific islands. In 1521, Magellan appeared among them. He was the first of a very well-documented group of European voyagers. They are usually called explorers, but I wonder if this is not the view of a later generation. Certainly the next few centuries show few evidences of deliberate exploration. Instead, we find that the Spanish ships which immediately followed paid absolutely no attention to the Pacific. Until about 1565, they sailed on the trade winds to the region found by Magellan and made no significant effort to find anything else. Why delay at tiny worthless islands when the riches of Asia were on the other side of the ocean? This attitude is reflected in the discoveries of the time. Most books show tracks of ships, and one gets the impression that vast regions were being explored. Actual discoveries of islands were confined almost entirely to the central western Pacific, but there they were very rapid. The far-flung Mariana, Caroline, and Marshall island groups were all discovered during the forty-three years after Magellan. Not all the islands, of course, but enough to identify the groups.

Sailing across the Pacific continued, but most ships were going to the same places and discoveries were few. The first Manila galleon crossed the Pacific from the Philippines to Mexico with a commercial cargo in 1565, long before the discovery of most of the islands. In 1578, Drake entered the Pacific to prey on Spanish ships in a highly profitable commercial venture of another sort, and still no one had ever looked for most of the islands. This is not the record of a deliberate or even an accidental program of exploration of the Pacific.

During the century from 1565 to 1650, three great regions of islands were found. The largest was a southeastern extension of the Spanish discoveries in the western Pacific. The Gilbert, Ellis, Tonga, New Hebrides, Solomon, Bismarck, and adjacent groups were found. Far to the south, Abel Tasman found, naturally, Tasmania and the western shore of New Zealand. In the central Pacific the Tuamotu and Marquesas groups were reconnoitered by ships sailing westward to populate or debauch the rich islands of the western seas.

Throughout this period we all have an impression of immense hardships. Scurvy, starvation, and thirst were not rare, although the experiences of Magellan were certainly extreme among the survivors. The point I should like to stress, however, is that the records of survivors are misleading. These voyagers were surrounded by the terror of the unknown. A significant fraction of the ships that entered the Pacific simply disappeared. The great killer was not malnutrition but shipwreck or foundering with loss of all hands. We may know this now, but at the time what horrors were suspected? Sea monsters? Cannibals? Reefs? Whirlpools? The modern sailor is wrapped and thoroughly lapped in knowledge of what is so and what is possible, and it is hard to conceive of the courage and endurance of the ancient mariners venturing into the unknown.

Wandering through the Pacific continued for one reason or another, but discoveries came at a slow pace. From 1650 to 1768 the only important island groups found were in a small region in the central Pacific, the groups now known as the Society, Samoan, and northern Cooks. An outstanding isolated discovery was Easter Island by Roggeveen, in 1722, who was looking for a large island or continent sighted by Davis somewhere in the eastern Pacific. The "somewhere" indicates one of the major sources of confusion during these times. Navigators could determine latitude with reasonable accuracy but frequently they misjudged longitude by several thousand miles. Consequently, the discoveries which we can now identify were rarely as clear to sailors at the time.

Two voyages also occurred in this period which resulted in fame and promotion for their leaders but little in the way of geographical information. In the time of George III certain geographers conceived that a great continent must exist in the South Pacific because otherwise the continents in the Northern Hemisphere would overweight the earth and turn it topsy-turvy. Considering the later history of this idea, it is clear why Newton, who understood something about gravity and the rotation of the earth, is buried in Westminster Abbey and the geographers are not. At the time however, it appeared that the existence of this continent was sufficiently probable to warrant searching for it in order to exploit its riches. Consequently,

England financed several expeditions for the purpose. The first was by John Byron, in 1764, who sailed around South America, went north to the trade winds, and crossed the Pacific to return home. He fathered the father of Lord Byron the poet, but was criticized by the Royal Society for ignoring his orders to discover something. In no wise discouraged (the first symptoms of regal insanity appeared in 1765), Captains Wallis and Carteret were sent out for the same purpose in 1767. Wallis discovered Tahiti, among other islands, while sailing northwest toward the Pacific trade winds, and Carteret went far enough south to find Pitcairn before heading home. England muddled through this series of adventures and misadventures and was rewarded by the services of the greatest of all Pacific explorers, Captain James Cook, who entered this ocean on the first of three voyages in 1769 and died at Hawaii a decade later. On the first of his Pacific voyages, Cook's principal responsibility was to make astronomical observations at Tahiti, whose discovery had just been announced by the returning Wallis. Consequently, he too entered the Pacific around Cape Horn and sailed to the northwest for a speedy landfall. Even so, he sailed far west of any previous voyage and thus missed no opportunity to achieve both his objectives. After leaving Tahiti, he did not follow his predecessors but went south to seek out the expected continent. He then explored New Zealand, proved that it was not the western margin of such a continent, and headed home. This was not only Cook's first Pacific expedition but in a very real sense the first Pacific scientific expedition, because the young man who would later be Sir Joseph Banks, president of the Royal Society, and a party of scientists and technicians were on board to make observations. Their results made Banks and Cook famous.

On his second voyage Cook again broke with tradition. He entered the Pacific from the west and thus had the prevailing westerly winds at his back as he searched for the expected southern continent. He made several great loops sailing east for long distances and then north to the trade winds in order to return to a position with the westerlies again at his back. By the time he was finished, the southern continent had become a myth. La Perouse, the French explorer directed to find the continent, said, "Mr. Cook has done so much that he has left me nothing to do but admire his work." Cook was unanimously elected a member of the Royal Society upon his return and received the Copley gold medal for the best experimental paper appearing that year.

He remained in England only eleven months before setting out on his third voyage, which took him to his death in the North Pacific. At the end of his exploration in 1779, it was known that the Pacific covered almost half of the world and contained no land approaching continental size. In a decade Cook had discovered most of the remaining island groups in this vast ocean, and the discovery phase of exploration of the tips of volcanoes and reefs protruding through the waters was essentially complete.

Stray islands continued to be found for the next eighty years, but most expeditions were directed toward science or detailed surveying rather than discovery. The accurate position of many islands is still questionable. The marine amphibious force which was directed in 1943 to land on Bougainville at dawn had some difficulty in planning the operation because the position of the shore was in doubt by ten miles. Even now when we put in to very remote islands, we sometimes make repeated celestial observations to try to improve the locations. This location problem is finally being solved by doing it in reverse, not by looking up at the stars but by looking down from them—using photographs from artificial satellites. I do not mean that this phase of the exploration of the Pacific was not without incident. One of the multitudinous facets of Cook was that he trained men who were as good as he was in some ways—but never in all. One was Captain William Bligh, maligned because of the mutiny on *H.M.S. Bounty*. Bligh and the loyal men made an incredible voyage in a small open boat. However, being a former lieutenant of Cook, he not only kept his men alive but also discovered, located, and sketched the shores of the main Fiji islands. We hoped to follow in his track in "Bligh Waters" on *Nova*.

The last island in the Pacific, Midway Island at the northern end of the Hawaiian chain, was discovered by Captain Brooks of the *Gambia* in 1859. It is a pleasing coincidence that the next and still continuing phase of exploration was initially based on an invention of passed Midshipman Brooke of the U.S. Navy. Three hundred years of exploration had found millions of square miles of water and a tiny area of land. Now it was time to explore the water and what was under it.

# *Scientific Exploration of the Pacific Ocean*

**CHAPTER THREE** One of my most distinguished colleagues at Scripps once designed a research ship. It was clear from the plans that none of the equipment would work when the ship was rolling in a normal swell. When queried, he explained that one could hardly expect a *real* scientist to work on something that pitched and rolled, and that the ship was a floating laboratory which would go to scientifically interesting places where the researchers would join it by airplane. The ship is a success.

Nevertheless, a very great scientist once sailed the Pacific and welcomed the opportunity even though he was wretched during every roll. Charles Darwin received a B.A. in theology, Euclid, and the Classics from Cambridge. By the time he was twenty-two, he had received some scientific training as an assistant to some very able men and knew how to stuff birds and collect fossils. As a result, on 24 August 1831, he received a letter from J. S. Henslow recommending that he take a position as unpaid naturalist on the circumnavigating voyage of *H.M.S. Beagle* with the words, "I have stated that I consider you to be the best qualified person I know of who is likely to undertake such a situation," a modest but realistic evaluation. Darwin first refused because his father had doubts about the merits of a position offered just before sailing. These doubts were resolved by family discussion, and young Darwin prepared to spend five years at sea on a small and overcrowded surveying ship. His accommodations consisted of a hammock and a few drawers in the chart room, although he did dine in the cabin with Captain Fitz-Roy, which gave him a "halo of sanctity" which caused the midshipmen to call him "Sir." He was ill during most of his later life and it is suspected that prolonged seasickness was at least a contributing cause. Oceanographers sometimes lie sick on the soaking deck of a ship until the moment required to make observations, then rise up, work, and lie down again. So it was with Darwin. On 25 April 1883, when he was about to be buried in Westminster Abbey, Admiral Lord Stokes wrote to the *Times* as follows:

> **We worked together for several years at the same table in the poop cabin of the *Beagle* during her celebrated voyage, he with his microscope and myself at the charts. It was often a very lively end of the little craft, and distressingly so to my old friend, who suffered greatly from sea-sickness. After perhaps an hour's work, he would say to me, "Old fellow, I must take the horizontal for it," that being the best relief position from ship motion; a stretch out on one side of the table for some time would enable him to resume his labours for a while, when he had again to lie down.**

On 9 June 1834, the *Beagle* entered the Pacific and remained on the Chile coast until September 1835. During that time, Darwin was much ashore observing the uplifted ancient shorelines, collecting fossils, and otherwise working as a young naturalist. By Christmas Day 1835, he was in New Zealand, having spent a few weeks in the Galapagos Islands, about ten days at Tahiti, and the remainder of the time at sea. In that brief period, he made the observations that led him gradually to the *Origin of Species* and the theory of evolution. He also began to formulate ideas on the origin of coral reefs and the development of volcanic islands which were to influence greatly the future understanding of the geological history of the ocean basins. Darwin visited only one atoll and that was in the Indian Ocean in 1836, but he saw many volcanic islands in various stages of development from active eruption to almost total destruction by wave and stream erosion. He published *The Structure and Distribution of Coral Reefs* in 1842 and therein set forth his celebrated theory of the origin of

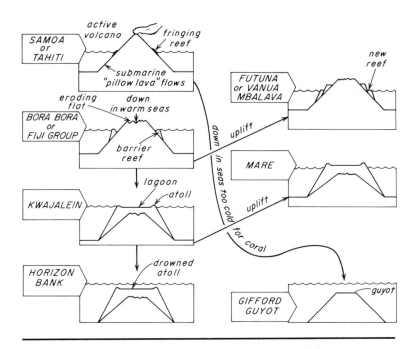

atolls. What he proposed was that some volcanoes grow up through several miles of water and become islands. When they become inactive, they are fringed by coral reefs if the ocean is warm enough. Then, he said, the volcanoes slowly sink and the reef grows upward so that a lagoon forms between reef and island. Finally, the volcano disappears, leaving a roughly circular lagoon within an almost continuous ring of coral reef. Previously, the prevailing idea about the origin of atolls had been that of the great geologist Lyell, who thought that the rings of coral marked the rims of submerged volcanic craters. Darwin had a copy of Lyell's *Principles of Geology* with him as a guide for his work on the *Beagle*. However, when Darwin returned, the master quickly accepted the ideas of the pupil, and Darwin's theory was off to a great start.

Not many scientists had either the grasp or vision of Lyell, and Darwin's ideas on coral reefs were hotly disputed. By the 1890s the Royal Society decided to resolve the matter by drilling an atoll to see whether it was a volcano capped by the thick coral demanded by Darwin's theory. I have not attempted to reconstruct the sequence of events whereby this drilling was brought about, but they cannot have been very different from the more familiar ones which occurred in the 1940s when the experiment was repeated by American scientists. Someone got the idea; a few friends and associates thought it was worth pursuing; the Royal Society appointed a committee to consider the matter; a recommendation was made to Her Majesty's Government to provide support; and another committee picked a drilling site after the most careful evaluation of available knowledge about atolls and the expectable results of drilling in various places. The site selected was the atoll of Funifuti and several holes were drilled in 1896–1898, the deepest to 1114½ feet with coral limestone at various places from top to bottom. It might seem that Darwin was confirmed, but critics quickly pointed out that below 300 feet all the corals were fragments which clearly had been rolled about. This meant that the hole might have been drilled in a capping of coral which had merely rolled down the side of a volcano. Submergence below 300 feet was still in doubt.

Most of Darwin's critics were concerned with the origin of the circular shape of atolls, whereas Darwin had been chiefly interested in whether large areas of the sea floor move up and down. Consequently, the scientific discussion in a remarkably large number of books was clouded by semantics. The matter was at last resolved when the atom bomb tests in the atolls of the Marshall Islands after World War II provided enough money for a thorough geological study. By this time the thickness of coral could be measured indirectly by geophysics and directly by the advanced drilling techniques developed to produce oil. Everything proved that Darwin was right. At Eniwetok Atoll the coral was almost a mile thick, and finally the drill brought up some basalt—the top of a volcano which had been near the sea surface more than 40 million years ago. With Darwin's theory of atoll formation confirmed, it was possible to turn to the, to me, more interesting question of movements of the sea floor. This will be one of the problems investigated during the *Nova* Expedition, so it is still not wholly resolved.

Between the *Beagle* and *Nova* the broad outlines of the

geology of the Pacific Basin were discovered. The earliest efforts to study the deep ocean began about the time that the last island was discovered in 1859. Much of this was in the North Atlantic, which was near the major scientific centers of Europe and where there was a great financial incentive to learn whether it was possible to lay a submarine telegraph cable to the United States. It was not too long before popular and political interest in oceanography was widespread on both sides of the ocean. Once, a line of deep sea soundings was made across the Atlantic on an American cruise which had the primary purpose of teaching a useful trade to the indigent orphans of Philadelphia.

The Pacific was more remote, but some oceanography was being done—notably in the preparation of charts of surface currents and the distribution of whales—by Matthew Fontaine Maury, the Superintendent of the Depot of Charts and Instruments of the U.S. Navy from 1842 to 1861. Maury set himself the task of making order out of the countless entries in American ships' logs. He compared the course a ship appeared to be steering according to its compass with the course it proved to have steered according to the next position determined by star sights. The difference indicated the drift of ocean currents at that time and place. By plotting all the sightings of whales, he mapped migration paths which took great schools across half the ocean at different seasons. His objectives were the support of American commerce and the Navy, but his methods earned him international esteem and cooperation. From 1842 to 1847, his office processed 26 million observations specially collected for him in the world oceans. In addition to this work, he made the broadest studies of the ocean from the data then available. By 1859, his *Physical Geography of the Sea* was in its sixth edition, and he knew everything there was to know on the subject. Except for the North Atlantic, all he could say at that time was:

> **The first specimens have been received from the coral sea of the Indian Archipelago and from the North Pacific. They were collected by the surveying expedition employed in those seas. A few soundings have been made in the South Atlantic but not enough to justify deduction as to its depths or the shape of its floor.**

This lack of knowledge led the Royal Society to send the *Challenger* Expedition around the world in 1872–1876. The ship was specially fitted out to sound and dredge in very deep water and was blessed with a captain who was a Fellow of the Royal Society. The ship displaced 2306 tons, which is far larger than most oceanographic ships now in use, but, of course, it was due to be away from its home port for a very long time. There were twenty-three officers and a large crew but only six scientists even though the objectives were wholly scientific. The chief scientist was Sir C. Wyville Thomson, who only reluctantly accepted such a lengthy assignment. The results of this expedition came out in a vast array of scientific volumes, logs, reminiscences, and popular accounts. Its scientific impact was enormous. The samples collected are still being used today. I have collected some fragments of the geological samples for study myself while in London. They are protected in an underground civil defense center, left over from the blitz, which is situated on the grounds of the British Museum, Natural History.

The ship departed England at 11:30 A.M. on Saturday, 21 December, which I find rather amusing because these days we hardly dare antagonize our crews by leaving or even arriving home on a weekend. Our ship *Argo* is due to return from the *Nova* Expedition on 18 December for no special reason except to have everyone home for Christmas. The attitudes of pioneers are understandably different from those of present oceanographers who go to sea again and again and again.

One of the junior scientists on the *Challenger* was Mr. John Murray. By 1908, he had become Sir John Murray K.C.B., L.L.D., F.R.S., and anyone who collected a deep sea bottom sample or even measured the depth, took care to send it to him at the Challenger Society Office in Edinburgh. Consequently, when we look at his maps of that date stating "compiled from the latest sources," we can be confident that they are complete. His chart of the Pacific shows about 500 soundings except in the southwestern Pacific to which I shall return. Of those in the deep open Pacific, almost all came from two sources: oceanographic expeditions and surveys for submarine telegraph cable routes. The chief oceanographic expeditions

were the *Challenger* itself which wandered from Australia to
New Zealand to Japan to Hawaii to Tahiti and on to Chile; and
various cruises of the *Albatross*. This later vessel belonged to
the U.S. Fish Commission and was under the scientific direction of Alexander Agassiz, son of Louis Agassiz, who founded
the Museum of Comparative Zoology at Harvard which published the records of this work. When the *Challenger* took the
first deep soundings in the southeastern Pacific, a broad elevation was discovered under the ocean. Inasmuch as no land
was nearby, this elevation was named the Albatross Plateau
after the only birds which frequent the region. When we were
once incidently following the approximate track of the *Challenger* from Tahiti to Valparaiso in 1958, I realized to my
surprise that we were in the most remote spot from land on
earth and once again there was no other life but the albatross.
It seemed particularly felicitous to Agassiz that he had available a ship called the *Albatross* with which to study the Albatross Plateau. The two ships took most of the soundings available in the region until after World War II when the U.S. Navy
began to provide logistic support for exploration of the Ant-
arctic and ran many sounding lines from the Panama Canal to
New Zealand.

The situation in the north and central Pacific was entirely
different. There bands of soundings are shown on Murray's
map along lines from the United States to Hawaii and thence
to Fiji and to Guam and the Philippines. Another line went
directly from Japan to Seattle. It will be apparent enough that
these were the major political and commercial centers in the
Pacific and that the routes were surveyed in order to pick locations for submarine cables. The surveys, seeking to avoid
great depths which would destroy the cables, found the deep
trenches that border the western Pacific. In its broad outlines,
the Pacific known to Murray was about the same as we know
sixty years later, but the "details" discovered since include
numerous mountain ranges as big as the Alps.

In a second map, Murray shows the distribution of the
curious sediments which he was first to discover in the Pacific.
These included volcanic and coral mud around islands which
were not very different from the muds and sedimentary rocks

found on continents. However, almost all of the deep sea floor was covered with very fine red clay and oozes consisting of the remains of microorganisms which live in the sea. These sediments were exceedingly rare on the continents and from this evidence alone, it seemed that the deep sea floor was never elevated above sea level and perhaps was eternally quiet and still. How different are the results and interpretations of modern research.

In an earlier report, Murray had described the sea floor relief and sediments of Melanesia which is to be the focus of the *Nova* Expedition. The cumulative effort of British surveys, chiefly along cable routes, is really astonishing for 1906. At that time, the oceanic soundings were so numerous that the 2000 plotted were only a small fraction of those available. There were 1019 measurements of the sea water temperature directly above the bottom and over 700 samples of bottom sediments. Murray was able to describe the general geography as:

> **extremely diversified, ridges and valleys running approximately in a north and south direction alternating with each other, the valley nearest Australia being the deepest.... This deep valley ... is broken up by several elevations which do not reach the surface of the sea, the latest additions to these elevations being the "Britannia Hills," discovered by Mr. Peake in 1903.**

Elucidating the origin of these very ridges and troughs and elevations is a major aim of *Nova*, and we hope to dredge the first samples of the Britannia Hills.

For almost forty years after Murray and Agassiz, little more was learned about the Pacific sea floor. Some samples of sediment were collected by the nonmagnetic ship *Carnegie* before she blew up in Apia harbor in 1929, but the invention of the echo sounder eliminated the opportunity to sample whenever a sounding was taken. Indeed, a large number of the new echo soundings were erroneous and, if anything, the oceanic charts of the Pacific in 1940 were worse than those of 1910. This was because measurement of depth with a wire was replaced by measuring the time it took an echo to bounce off the sea floor. This was tricky even when done by skilled scientists and almost beyond the capabilities of the sailors who made many of the measurements as an extra duty while standing watch. A friend of mine once met such a sailor in a bar in San Diego and was told that his normal practice was to ignore the sounder and just record the same depth as the sailor who had been on duty for the previous four hours. Even more conscientious men could rarely do much with mysterious beeps and flashing red lights which were supposed to tell the depth.

The marvels of technology developed by the Navy to look for submarines in the 1940s changed everything, and ships, instruments, and money became available for modern oceanography. The first work in the Pacific, however, was done as a part of three world-circling expeditions by British, Swedish, and Danish scientists, some of whom had used their time during the war to make preparations. The first was the Swedish *Albatross* (once again that wonderful name) Expedition of 1947–1948 headed by Hans Pettersson. Superficially, it seemed a little like the *Challenger* Expedition in that a small number of scientists were on a large and carefully outfitted ship. However, the problems of interest and the equipment to study them were very different indeed. The ship had a special winch with a great tapered wire capable of reaching the deepest parts of the sea. It had a newly invented corer which could plunge a steel pipe 30 to 60 feet into the sea floor, which previously had only been scraped. It had devices to measure the thickness of sediment between the sea floor and the hard igneous rock of the oceanic crust, and the amount of heat flowing through the sea floor because of the decay of radioactive minerals in the interior of the earth. And, wonder of wonders, it had an echo sounder which recorded a continuous profile of depths and thus gave a real picture of the shape of the sea floor. I can still remember the excitement when Robert Dietz and I first projected microfilms of these precious records in 1950. Now just my own collection of such depth recordings would form a continuous strip more than 100 miles long, and our Scripps fleet sometimes records 10 million soundings in a month.

With all these new devices, the Swedish scientists discovered undersea mountains and traced the fluctuations in oceanic sedimentation produced by variations in ocean currents during the last million years. They also found that the sediment in ocean basins was by no means as thick as was expected, considering that rivers had emptied into them for billions of years. Moreover, their measurements suggested that the same amount of heat was flowing up through the oceanic crust as through the continents. This was completely contrary to all expectations because the radioactive minerals which produce the heat appear to be concentrated in continents. All in all, the results were extremely exciting for geologists and geophysicists and stimulated work which still continues.

The Danish *Galathea* Expedition of 1950–1952 was headed by another famous scientist, Anton Bruun, whose name now graces a ship dedicated to international oceanographic research and cooperation. The expedition was partially financed by the Carlsberg Brewery in Copenhagen, which had supported research at sea on previous occasions. The objectives were primarily biological and were spectacularly successful. *Galathea* dredged animals from the deepest trenches and off Central America found a "living fossil," an animal of a type which was previously known only in rocks tens of millions of years old.

The last of these three circumnavigating expeditions was British and named *Challenger II*, but unlike its predecessor its primary aim was surveying possible hazards to navigation. One can only shudder at the story that the ship had been presented with a complete set of the great volumes of scientific results of the *Challenger* Expedition and that one day someone threw the lot overboard because the old books were taking up space. Perhaps this was apocryphal; in any event, very valuable measurements were made of the thickness of the crust of various ocean basins, which turned out to be much thinner than continents.

About this time, the general complexion of oceanography in the Pacific, and elsewhere, began to change. No longer was it assumed that each expedition would be followed by years of study of samples before planning began for the next one. Russia and the United States almost simultaneously began a truly massive assault on the ocean basins which continues to intensify. From 1949 through 1958, the Russian Institute of Oceanology ship *Vityaz* participated in twenty-five major voyages and the Scripps ship *Horizon* must have done about the same. Considering all the ships belonging to the two institutions, the total number of Pacific expeditions surely exceeded one hundred in a decade, and many other institutions in several nations were also active. Now there are always half a dozen oceanographic ships at sea in the Pacific. In 1960, we visited what we looked upon as a very remote island indeed, taking care to bring magazines and newspapers for the few scientists stationed there. It turned out that we were the third oceanographic ship to visit the island in a week.

# Objectives of the Expedition

**CHAPTER FOUR** The *Nova* Expedition includes many independent scientific experiments on land, sea, and air. Some of the studies are only very broadly related, and describing the reasons for and expectations from each would take an encyclopedia. These programs are part of the expedition only because ships are expensive and we try to make our operations as varied and efficient as possible. However, most of the investigations are parts of an integrated study of a general problem, namely, the origin and geological history of continents and ocean basins. This includes such questions as: Do continents drift about on the surface of the earth? Do continents grow and shrink? Are they torn into fragments by the convective flow of rocks within the interior of the earth? Does the sea floor move from one place to another? And so on. These ideas may seem a little bizarre even to people who know that the elements are transmutable and are prepared to believe that the universe is expanding. I shall have to review some recent geological discoveries in order to explain why they are taken seriously and thus how we hope to test them.

To begin with, we may consider the origin of the continents and ocean basins. In attempting to answer this question, scientists have used their imaginations to the fullest to make up for a paucity of facts. It is known that continents and ocean basins are very different but they float on a common material

called the mantle. The top of the mantle is called the Moho-
rovičić discontinuity or more usually just the Moho. The deep
structure of the crust and mantle is measured by the way
shock waves move through it. For example, a hydrogen bomb
test can be detected on seismographs all over the earth. The
types of waves detected and their time of arrival indicates that
in the upper part of the mantle the pressure wave velocity is
about eight kilometers per second in most places. The bottom
of the continental or oceanic crust is defined as the depth at
which this velocity is detected. The thickness of the continents
is about twenty miles and the oceanic crust is only about three
miles. This is the reason that the Mohole Project planned to
drill to the mantle through the ocean floor instead of through
a continent. Not only are the thicknesses very different but so
are most other things. The rocks of the continents are light-
colored and the oceanic ones are dark—a fact which reflects
their very different composition. The concentration of heat-
generating radioactive minerals in continental rocks is much
higher than in oceanic ones, for example. Even the age of the
rocks is different. The continents contain rocks more than 3
billion years old, but the oldest rocks found in ocean basins
are no older than 200 million years, or less than a tenth as
much.

How did these two very different types of material come
to be on the surface of one planet? One group of ideas involves celestial catastrophes. It has been proposed that the
continents are asteroids which hit an earth which was once all
ocean basin. A diametrically opposed view is that the earth
was once completely covered with continent and that part of
it was pulled away to form the moon or that several parts of
it were blasted away by the explosive impact of asteroids.
Quite a different type of idea is that the earth was once covered entirely by continent but has been, and is, expanding
and that the ocean basins are the opening cracks between
continental fragments. Finally, there is the hypothesis that
everything on the surface of the earth is the froth produced by
gradual migration of low-density material from the interior.
This idea has the great virtue that it accounts not only for continental rocks but also for sea water, which is another light-

weight material. Having extracted the materials it is still necessary to sort them into continents and oceanic crust and sea water, but all of geological time is available for the purpose.

At present, no one is sure which of these ideas is correct. All may have had some effect, but which have been important? This is the sort of problem which perhaps will be answered only when we have more information about other planets and the moon.

On a more modest scale we may wonder what has happened to the continents and oceanic crust since they were formed. Many geologists think that the continents have grown. Lava comes from the mantle and volcanoes spread it on the surface of continents. Consequently, new continental material is accumulating even now. Similar volcanic rocks have flowed out for several billion years. If the rate in the past was the same as during historical times, this vulcanism alone could have produced the whole volume of the continental crust and probably sea water as well. There is also a suggestion that the area of continents has increased because the oldest rocks, in North America at least, are in the center and younger ones lie closer to the edge. As we might expect, considering the speculation involved, the alternative idea that the continents are now shrinking has also been suggested. This is one of the possible interpretations of the fact that many mountain ranges simply disappear when they come to the edge of a continent and that many sedimentary rocks seem to have been eroded from mountains located where ocean basins now exist.

Another way to explain this same evidence is to say that continents which are now widely separated were once joined together and thus that the continuations of the mountain ranges, for example, still exist but are now separated by an oceanic gap. This is the famous theory of continental drift proposed in its best-known form by Alfred Wegener fifty years ago. Wegener started with the fact that the Atlantic sides of Africa and South America can be fitted together with hardly any gaps or overlap. This can be seen on any world map. He also noted that very peculiar and distinctive plants flourished in Africa, southern South America, and India at about the same time in the geological past. Likewise, evidence of more

By permission of the Royal Society

or less simultaneous glaciation occurred in these places and Australia at about the same time. He argued that a vast southern continent once existed and had broken up and spread apart about 100 million to 200 million years ago. This idea was greeted with an understandable skepticism, especially when it developed that the mechanisms which he proposed for producing the drift were quite improbable. For forty years his ideas were generally accepted in the Southern Hemisphere, where geologists could look at the evidence he advanced. Acceptance in Europe was mixed. It was minimal in the United States.

Then a new approach developed, based on the discovery that the position of the ancient magnetic pole was preserved in different types of rocks regardless of age. Although the origin of the earth's magnetic field is still somewhat obscure, for the last 60 million years the magnetic poles have corresponded roughly with the poles of rotation. Thus, the magnetic pole positions evident in the rocks probably indicate the approximate position of the geographic pole. The new magnetic data suggest widespread drift of continents and that the various components of Wegener's great southern continent, "Gondwanaland," were very near the southern pole at the time of the glaciation. Many ambiguities were discovered, and doubtful geologists had reason for continuing skepticism, but it was quite striking that the new type of observations strongly supported continental drift as originally conceived on quite different evidence.

In the late 1950s it was discovered that an enormous mountain range lies in the center of most ocean basins and particularly in those basins which separate the supposed fragments of Gondwanaland. The suggestion was rapidly advanced that this mountain range, or midocean ridge system, marked the initial crack along which Gondwanaland had split and from which the fragments had spread. The ultimate confirmation of this idea required large-scale investigations of the sea floor and a gradual understanding of how the midocean ridge system develops. To a certain extent, marine geology during the past two decades has only accidentally provided evidence bearing on this question, which is hardly surprising because the question itself is not that old. In more recent years, however, considerable effort has been spent in trying to answer this question with the happy result that the answer is now known.

How this came about involves a brief history of the course of oceanographic exploration and the development of ideas and hypotheses to explain the observations. The first hundred years of oceanographic research contributed hardly anything that is of interest except the discovery of deep sea trenches and parts of the midocean ridge system. In 1940, it appeared that the sea floor was a relatively quiet place with minimal relief and that all mountain building and other important geological processes occurred on continents or at their margins. During World War II came the first breakthrough because Professor Harry Hess of Princeton happened to be navigator and later captain of the *U.S.S. Cape Johnson,* a Navy supply ship plying the western Pacific. He kept the recording echo sounder on his ship operating in deep water where most ships turned them off. The result was the discovery of deeply submerged volcanoes with flat tops which he called "guyots" after Guyot Hall where his office is situated at Princeton. He immediately made the correct interpretation that guyots are truncated volcanoes which had been eroded flat when they formerly were islands, even though they are now at depths as great as a mile below sea level. It was clear that the sea floor was far more active than anyone had believed.

Shattered beliefs soon became a commonplace as it developed that almost everything supposed about ocean basins was wrong. The crust under ocean basins is not as thick as continental crust but in fact is much thinner and also astonishingly uniform. The sediment in the basins is not a mile or more thick as anticipated from the known rate of erosion of continents. Instead it is only a thousand feet thick, which is the amount of sediment that would accumulate in only a few hundred million years rather than in the total age of the earth. Moreover, no really ancient rocks can be found in the basins comparable to the three-billion-year-old rocks of the continents. At first, this was attributed to inadequate sampling but as the number of bottom samples continued to mount, the suspicion grew that ocean basin rocks are all relatively young. The midocean ridge system was found to be the locus of many earthquakes and a great trough was discovered running along the crest of the Mid-Atlantic Ridge. Soon a belt of unprecedentedly high heat flow was found along the crest of the midocean ridges.

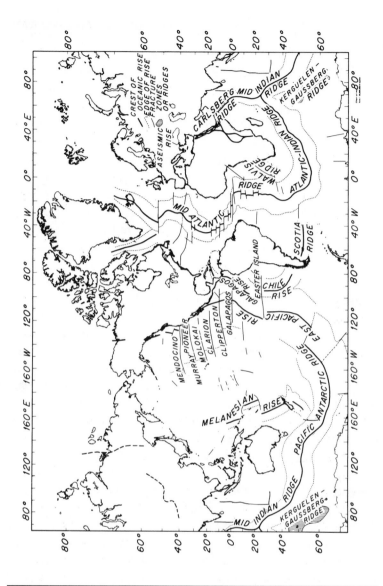

All of these features were accepted as evidence of modern mountain building and the supposedly quiet ocean basins began to emerge as the very focus of global deformation. The largest faults on the surface of the earth were discovered in the Pacific, features thousands of miles long which follow straight lines even when plotted on a globe. Similar faults were soon found extending across the Atlantic ocean basin and indeed everywhere on the flanks of the midocean system.

Patterns of magnetic anomalies were discovered in the northeastern Pacific which have the peculiar properties that they are perpendicular to the great faults and are offset along them. That is, a distinctive anomaly can be traced to a fault and then is found again on the other side but displaced by a great distance. The maximum displacement is 700 miles. A comparable discovery on land would be that a road in California would stop at a great crack and that when this crack was traced to the east, a continuation of the road would appear in Utah. No such offset has been found anywhere on the continents and, once again, the sea floor assumed more importance in geological thinking.

As oceanographers made these discoveries, they proposed explanations but they were very specific—the number of explanations was at least equal to the types of facts and no common unifying hypotheses were proposed. After a while broader syntheses were attempted and they succeeded in explaining large groups of facts. One such idea, that the earth is rapidly expanding, could explain young ocean basins, thin sediment, and the position, topography, and earthquakes of the midocean ridge system. Another idea, mantle convection rising and spreading from the centers of the midocean ridge system, offered an explanation for most of the same features and also for the orientation and length of great oceanic faults, the surprising equality of average continental and ocean heat flow, the high heat flow near the crest of rises and ridges, and the tendency for large regions of the sea floor to sink.

However, it remained for the same Harry Hess who discovered guyots to propose a truly comprehensive hypothesis which explained just about everything known, and as it turned out, was capable of explaining many things discovered later. Hess rarely goes to sea on an oceanographic ship any more and thus this is a classic example of a broad synthesis created by someone who is not involved with the trivia which blind people who are involved with day-to-day collection of data. The example is highly exceptional, however, because the synthesizer was also a pioneer data collector in the same field more than two decades earlier.

Hess proposes that convection currents in the mantle rise

under the midocean ridge system and spread toward the margins. This is a concept that he and others have been developing for several years and which could explain a variety of major features of the ocean basins. The inspiration that he added was that the oceanic crust is not merely stretched over midocean ridges but is actually created there. Hess is interested not only in marine geology but also in the origin and composition of the little-known rocks of the mantle. His investigations have led him to the conclusion that the upper mantle is probably made of peridotite, a dense rock rich in magnesium. It is commonly found at the surface of continents in places which were once deep in the crust and which have been elevated and eroded. It also occurs as fragments in lava flows which have come from the mantle. Thus, it appears that it is an important constituent of the interior of the earth. This peridotite has the interesting property that in some circumstances if it combines with water at a temperature below 500°C, it forms a new rock, serpentine, and that if reheated the water is driven out and it again is peridotite.

Hess conceived that peridotite and water in the mantle convect upward along lines under the ocean basins and elevate the midocean ridge system. As the mantle moves upward, it cools and passes through the level which is at 500°C, and the water and peridotite combine and form serpentine. Laboratory tests indicate that whereas peridotite transmits earthquakes with the velocity of the mantle, serpentine transmits them like the oceanic crust. Consequently, Hess had a mechanism for producing crust from mantle as a consequence of the convection which was already suggested by many types of evidence. But now he could explain many new things. The oceanic crust has its astonishingly uniform thickness because it is formed above a certain temperature which occurs at a uniform depth. The crust can move very large distances without leaving central gaps because new crust forms at the center of spreading. It does not pile up in great thicknesses at the edges of the ocean basins because as it is pushed down below the 500°C level, it is reconverted to peridotitic mantle. Continents do not drift through the mantle but merely float on it as it moves away from rises and ridges.

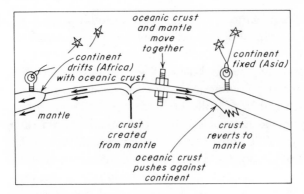

**The sea floor spreading hypothesis.**

The theory can also explain many other things provided the duration of the most recent mantle convection is known. The evidence available is rather tenuous but it suggests that most of the sea floor has been produced in this way during the last few hundred million years. For example, the Atlantic Ocean apparently was opened by continental drift during that time. If so, the oceanic sediment is thin because it is sitting on a young crust and has not had much time to accumulate. This does not mean that all ocean *basins* are necessarily very young but merely that older sediment has been skimmed off and plastered against the continents while older crust has been reconverted into mantle. The elimination of older crust likewise explains why no old rocks are found in ocean basins no matter how many times they are sampled. The older rocks have been moved out of ocean basins and either pushed into continents or pulled down into the mantle where they cannot be dredged.

Although an impressive display of imagination, this idea, soon named the "sea floor spreading hypothesis" by Robert Dietz, did not quickly gain acceptance. Geologists and geophysicists on average are as conservative in their own fields as any other group. It is hard enough adjusting to a growing flood of new work and ideas which surely are proven without also trying to understand the implications of everything which is not proven. The sea floor spreading hypothesis was not the only explanation for each of the things it explained, and it did not seem to agree with the details of many observations. Acceptance required some precise confirmation which was incompatible with all other ideas about the sea floor. An even slightly ambiguous confirmation would not do. When I was a student, Professor Kirk Bryan at Harvard once told me, "Sometime you may be lucky enough to get a revolutionary idea and prove it is right, but don't expect that it will be immediately acclaimed. Students may accept it but you will have to wait until the older geologists die off before everyone agrees it is right."

The confirmation of sea floor spreading came from the proof of a really outlandish corollary. Fred Vine and Drummond Matthews, respectively a graduate student and young instructor at Cambridge University, suggested that the spreading sea floor is a tape recorder. About the time Hess published his hypothesis, it was being established that the magnetic field of the earth is periodically reversed. Certain iron-rich minerals in solidifying volcanic rocks become oriented in the direction of the earth's magnetic field. When the rocks cool through the Curie point the orientation of the magnetic minerals is fixed and cannot readily be altered without reheating. Thus by measuring the direction of magnetization of the minerals in an ancient rock it is possible to determine the location of the magnetic north pole at the time the rock cooled. When the position of the pole was studied in detail in a given locality, it appeared that the north and south magnetic poles occasionally reversed. This was rapidly explained in several different ways and the significance of the observations was obscure. The field measurements continued and more effort was made to date the time of reversals by newly refined methods of measuring rock ages by the decay of radioactive elements. The origin of the reversals was established in an elegant way when it was gradually proved that the reversals occurred at the same time in widely separated places. That is, there were several distinct and worldwide times of reversal which could only mean that the whole magnetic field had reversed during a period of a few thousand years. It is interesting to speculate how navigation would have been affected if the field had been reversing,

as it will again, during the last 1000 years. If the reversal occurs in jumps, or if it starts and stops, there would have been
a lot of lost sailors and much more actuarial and scientific
interest in magnetism.

Vine and Matthews reasoned that the long parallel magnetic anomalies characteristic of the oceanic rises and ridges
are produced by reversals of the magnetic field combined with
sea floor spreading. The lava that pours out and cools in the
center of a rise preserves a record of the orientation of the
magnetic field at that time. Spreading splits the solidified lava
and moves it to the flanks of the rise. Meanwhile, the widening
gap is again filled with cooling lava. If the magnetic field reverses during this period, the newer rocks preserve a record
of a reversed field. Field measurements of the present total
intensity of the field would show a strong field where the
present one is reinforced by an ancient field with the same
polarity and a weakened field where the modern and ancient
field are in opposite directions. A tape recorder works in the
same way, preserving the intensity of a varying magnetic field
to which the moving tape is exposed.

Within a few years two new facts about the long parallel
magnetic anomalies were discovered and both agreed exactly
with the tape recorder hypothesis. First, it was found that the
anomalies, which have quite distinctive shapes, are symmetrical around the centers of rises and ridges; in short, the sea floor
is a *stereo* tape recorder with almost identical volcanic rock
"tapes" spreading out in enormous sheets from the center. This
was beyond the fondest expectations of Vine and Matthews
because no one ever conceived of the enormous mountain-
building deformation of the earth behaving in such a remarkably orderly manner. In any event, the idea of the moving
crust preserving a history of reversals of the earth's magnetic
field is the only one that offers a reasonable explanation for
the symmetry. The other discovery was that the distance between the sea floor anomalies is generally proportional to the
spacing between the times of reversals of the magnetic field
measured on land during the last 3 million years. Consequently, particular sea floor anomalies can be paired with
particular reversals. This not only reconfirms that the anoma-

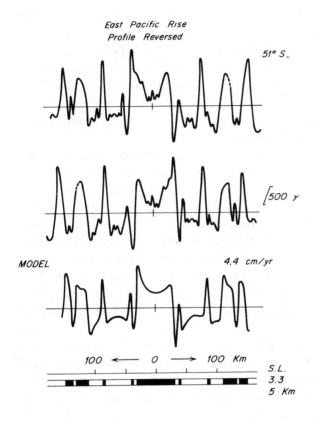

East Pacific Rise
Profile Reversed

51° S.

500 γ

MODEL                                    4.4 cm/yr

100 ←      0      → 100 Km

S.L.
3.3
5 Km

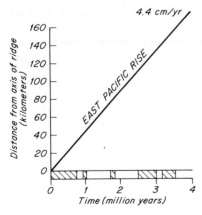

4.4 cm/yr

EAST PACIFIC RISE

Distance from axis of ridge (kilometers)

Time (million years)

lies are produced by reversals but gives the speed at which the "tape" is moving and shows that it moves at a relatively constant speed for long periods. The sea floor is spreading away from the center at about one-half inch per year in the North Atlantic and almost two inches per year in the South Pacific. These are about the right rates to open up the whole Atlantic Basin in the time since Africa and South America were apparently joined together.

The origin of these magnetic anomalies confirmed Hess's hypothesis of sea floor spreading and numerous other confirmations followed in short order. J. Tuzo Wilson of the University of Toronto observed that the large earthquakes along the great sea floor faults which offset the center of midocean ridges have a very peculiar distribution. The faults are thousands of miles long, but the earthquakes generally occur only between the offset centers of the rises. He reasoned that if the sea floor is spreading from each of the offset centers, this distribution can be explained. Between the centers, the oceanic crust on the two sides of the fault is moving in opposite directions, and this causes earthquakes. Beyond the centers, however, the crust on both sides of the fault is moving in the same direction and no earthquakes occur. If this is correct, it means that the motion on the faults is in the opposite direction from the indicated offset of the centers of a rise. He assumed that the faults are very old and that the younger rises and ridges were offset

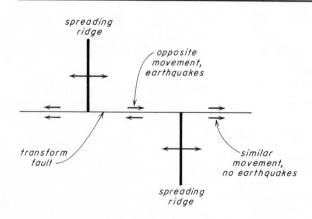

when they were created by convection. He did not attempt to explain the origin of the faults or the offsets, merely the earthquakes. His prediction of the direction of motion of the crust was subject to testing because the first motion on earthquakes can be measured by studying the motion they produce in instruments on land. Lynn Sykes of Lamont Geological Observatory quickly proved that Wilson was right and, since the prediction assumed sea floor spreading, also proved that Hess was right.

Shortly everyone got into the act. Vast quantities of oceanographic observations were available to evaluate the reality of sea floor spreading. The thickness of sediment increases at greater distances from the centers of spreading. Although no fossils in ocean basins are very old by geological standards, the oldest ones occur at the margins of parts of the sea floor that have spread, and younger and younger fossils are found as the centers of spreading are approached. There is even a correlation with the rate of spreading. The solidified lavas are thick where spreading is slow and they are thin where it is fast. Likewise, mountainous ridges and a central rift are associated with slow spreading and low rolling hills with fast spreading. Most of the topography of the sea floor, like the magnetic anomalies and crust, is formed at the center of a rise or ridge and then spreads to one side or the other.

These correlations and confirmations of sea floor spreading have appeared very rapidly and are still coming. As I write this in preparation for the *Nova* Expedition, many of these discoveries have yet to be published in the scientific literature. Thus we go to sea in a time of great intellectual ferment and excitement. What remains to be done? For one thing, we have before us the opportunity to prove that more than one period of convection has occurred during the history of the earth. This is a particularly important point because our present knowledge about sea floor spreading is concerned with only the last small fraction of geological time. We need quite different information to tell whether the same process has occurred again and again, sweeping the sea floor clean and causing continents to drift about during the last several billion years.

The most favorable place to look for such evidence is in the region between Hawaii and the southwestern Pacific which we shall be traversing repeatedly during *Nova*. In this region it appears that about 100 million years ago the sea floor was elevated into a broad oceanic rise which has since slowly subsided. Charles Darwin first observed that this region had subsided, and consequently this broad feature is called the Darwin Rise in his honor. Since Darwin's time, Hess and various following oceanographers have found and dredged numerous drowned ancient islands in this region. The few that are sampled were islands at about the same time.

The load of these ancient islands cracked the surrounding crust and enormous volumes of volcanic rock poured out of the cracks. Then the rise sank. But was it really a rise like the existing ones, and will the Mid-Atlantic Ridge and the East Pacific Rise sink like the Darwin Rise? It is now clear that one

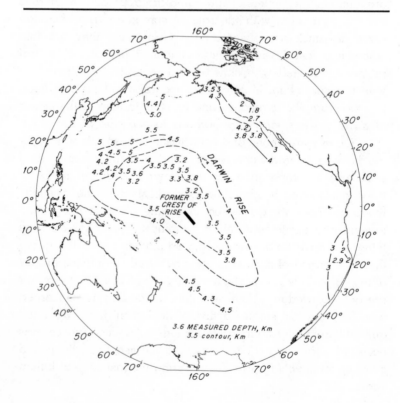

of the most powerful geological tests for the former existence of a rise like modern ones is the discovery of long parallel magnetic anomalies distributed symmetrically around the supposed ancient center of the rise. A few magnetic profiles across the Darwin Rise indicate anomalies with the right shapes and sizes. In one small area they are at least slightly linear. Our ship tracks are laid out to fill in gaps and to try to see whether there is an integrated, symmetrical anomaly pattern. If found it will be very important because almost inevitably it will be older than the patterns associated with the sea floor spreading of the last 100 million years. This is not certain because we do not know for sure that the present period of spreading has existed for only 100 million years—but it seems probable. Since the Darwin Rise started to die and sink at about that time, its magnetic anomalies would be older. If we are very lucky we shall find that the magnetic anomalies are symmetrical and that the ones in the center of the Darwin Rise are the same as those on the outer flanks of the existing rises and ridges. Then we can be sure that the ancient and modern rises have the same development and see how they are related. We shall also know whether rises are ephemeral and may have existed at different times in the past.

Of course, we cannot expect too much of six profiles measuring magnetic anomalies, and we may not be much further along toward solving these problems next fall than we are now. If so, we shall have to return. One of the complications making it difficult to map magnetic anomalies is that they are so commonly offset along perpendicular faults. If the faults are not located, it is difficult to determine the trends of anomalies. Unfortunately, it is not easy to map faults and anomalies at the same time because they are mutually perpendicular. If we go in one direction, we cross anomalies but not faults; and if we go in the other, we cross only faults and run along the anomalies, which is not much help. Some faults are already mapped, however, and they will help us determine what has happened and where to explore. The faults themselves are not without interest because they are so long and straight, and in some places they have formed very deep troughs. One just east of the Phoenix Islands is almost 25,000 feet deep and the bottom is far down in the oceanic crust. By dredging the cliffs on each side of this trough, we hope to get samples which in most places would be obtainable only by very expensive drilling through the unfaulted crust. Thus, if we are successful and the wire does not break and fresh rock is exposed on the cliffs, we shall know the composition of the crust and see whether Hess is right in his prediction of serpentine, as he has been right in so many other things.

The sea floor spreading hypothesis will also provide a guide for our studies of the southwestern Pacific, and in that region we shall have information from islands to guide us. In fact, the great peculiarity of Melanesia is that it is a jumble of large continental islands and small ocean basins on a scale which exists nowhere else on earth. The Pacific edges of Melanesia generally are marked by "island arcs," which is the geological term for chains of volcanic and uplifted coral islands bordered by a very deep oceanic trench and with associated earthquakes. These island arcs are different from others around the margins of the Pacific. The Tonga-Kermadec "arc," for example, is straight except at the northern end where it curves sharply to the west. In other respects, it is relatively normal in that the trench is on the Pacific side of the islands and the earthquakes dip from near the surface below the trench to about 400 miles below the sea floor west of the islands. Dipping planes marked by earthquakes of this sort occur only below island arcs or continental equivalents, and they are usually intepreted as faults on which the islands are being pushed over the trenches. Most dip away from the Pacific, but in this respect, the island arcs of northwestern Melanesia are peculiar. The New Britain, Solomon, and New Hebrides arcs are linked in a wavy chain. The trenches next to these arcs are all on the side away from the Pacific Basin and the fault planes all dip toward the basin. Everything is backward, and the cause for this is one of the puzzles that besets us.

Many puzzles exist regarding the small faults at the top of the crust around island arcs, and these will be studied to see what they reveal about the existence of deep thrusting and the formation of trenches. The filling of trenches by sediment is also little understood and will be elucidated by mapping and sampling the small basins filled with sediment on the sides and in the bottom of the trench. We shall also measure the heat flow to see how it varies from place to place and take photographs to try to find bare rock to dredge. Very peculiar rocks, which appear to be typical of the lower parts of the crust, have been dredged in other trenches and may occur here exposed in the walls of the trench.

Between the island arcs and Australia are the small continents and ocean basins of prime interest to *Nova*. The islands of New Zealand, the Fijis, and New Caledonia have been mapped by geologists and are relatively well known compared to the sea floor. They are considered to be little continents because they are above sea level and because they consist of rocks which occur in typical continents but not in ocean basins. Most of the rocks are produced by weathering and redeposition and sometimes reheating of fragments derived from older volcanic outpourings and intrusions of igneous rock. What are the sources from which the sediments were eroded? The geologists who have mapped Fiji are inclined to believe that the sources were all local and that erosion and redeposition have merely shifted sediment from one place to another on the islands. All the rocks in Fiji seem to be relatively young, and shifting them about does not seem unreasonable. New Caledonia is much more puzzling. Many of the rocks are much older, and they were deposited in an elongate submarine trough which was at least as extensive as the present island. Where did the sediments come from to fill the trough, if the present island was all under water? New Caledonian geologists tend to call on a former bordering mountain range which has now disappeared. There are two possible positions for this former range. If New Caledonia has not moved, then the range has been changed into the deep ocean basin which is now west of the island. However, continental drift is another possibility. Perhaps New Caledonia was once next to Australia or perhaps next to a supposed continent midway between the present positions of Australia and New Caledonia. New Zealand is more like New Caledonia than Fiji, and many geologists think that it, too, derived sediment from a source which has sunk or drifted away. The concept of one or more sunken continents in Melanesia has been stated repeatedly and for convenience I shall merely refer to a continent "Melantis," which not only sounds similar to Atlantis but has some of the same connotations of doubtful existence.

In a few months we can hardly expect to do much productive work on these islands because it has taken many years to learn the little that is already known.

Mostly we shall try to solve the problems of the land by looking at the sea floor between islands. This may seem rather indirect, but it has been a revealing approach in other regions. We shall map the topography, measure the thickness of the layers of the crust, measure variations of the magnetic and gravity fields, determine heat flow, and obtain samples of sediment and rock. Hardly anything is known about the Melanesian ocean basin because of a peculiarity of oceanographic exploration. The general topography and sediment distribution were discovered early because of the necessity of laying submarine telegraph cables. Since the development of modern marine geology, however, the region has largely been skirted. It is extremely distant from the older Pacific oceanographic centers in the United States, Siberia, and Japan; and the newer centers in New Zealand, Australia, and New Caledonia are only beginning to develop the necessary technology. Fortunately, a special international effort was made to study the even more remote Indian Ocean a few years ago. Much was learned along the tracks of ships going to and from the Indian Ocean. Even so, Melanesia was almost completely neglected because the ships had to go either north or south of Australia and Melanesia is, so to speak, in a lee of the continent. All we have are a few intriguing clues regarding what we may find.

We know more about the bottom topography of Melanesia than anything else, but we do not know enough for our purposes. The older spot soundings simply do not give the same kind of information as modern, recorded echo soundings. Older methods yielded a generalized map. New ones produce a continuous picture of the sea floor under a moving ship. The difference in what can be learned is about the same as the difference between looking at the moon with the naked eye and taking pictures of it with a rocket which flies just above it. We have

to know exactly what the bottom looks like in order to plan all
our other work because everything depends on the depth and
relief, whether mountainous or smooth. Mountains are interesting because they indicate the nature and orientation of the
deforming forces which produced them. Mountains can be
formed by vertical uplift or horizontal squeezing or stretching,
and each type looks somewhat different. The smooth plains
are also interesting because they result from burial of hills by
sediment or very fluid lava flows. Near continents almost all
smoothing is by sediment which flows out from rivers and
beaches, moves along the sea floor, and comes to rest in deep
basins and troughs. Such flat-floored basins occur east of Australia and New Guinea, south of Fiji, and in various directions
around New Zealand. The movement of sediment described is
not unreasonable because it is all downhill and thus aided by
gravity. In fact, the deposition of sediment on the steep submarine slopes around continents might seem unlikely, but it
has occurred in the Coral Sea southeast of New Guinea. For
some reason sediment has collected in and filled an arm of a
basin between New Guinea and the deep sea floor instead of
continuing to move downhill. We hope to find out why. One
possibility is that the deep basin has been created by continental drift since the arm was filled. That is, the area itself was
the deepest place available when it was filled. We can get
some indications of what happened in the past by studying
what is happening now. For this purpose we shall collect sediment from the rivers and beaches of New Guinea. Different
rivers drain different source regions and hence may transport
quite different and distinctive minerals. We shall take sedimentary cores of the Coral Sea floor and compare the minerals
obtained with those from the rivers. This may show from
whence and how the abyssal sediments are deposited.

With the echo sounder we can also try to find flat-topped
submarine volcanoes, guyots, like those first discovered by
Harry Hess in the central Pacific. A few have already been
found in the deep Tasman Basin east of Australia. They lie
along a straight line about midway between the Australian
coast and the Lord Howe Rise, and their history, can we but
discover it, will tell us much about what has happened in this

part of Melanesia. The Lord Howe Rise itself is strikingly flat on top in an area 60 miles wide and more than 100 miles long. Even though it is now a little more than half a mile below sea level, this great area may have been planed flat by waves and rivers if it was above sea level at some time in the past. Extensive truncation on this scale has occurred in the region east of New Zealand which is now at a considerable depth. Another possibility is that the Lord Howe Rise was once mountainous and that the valleys or troughs have been filled with sediment. Shallow areas of the sea floor in warm equatorial waters typically are covered with microscopic shells of Foraminifera, which are animals that are very abundant in surface waters. When they die, the shells fall to the sea floor but are dissolved in very deep water and preserved only on highs.

We shall have no difficulty distinguishing a blanket of sediment from truncated rock on the Lord Howe Rise because we shall make continuous profiles of the upper layers of the sea floor. This is done with instruments like echo sounders but more powerful. A loud noise can be generated in the sea in many ways: by explosives, by electrical sparks, by igniting blobs of natural gas, or by compressed air bursts. We use an electrical spark for the gear on *Horizon* and compressed air on *Argo*. This is because these sub-bottom profilers, now abbreviated to "profilers," are still in experimental development and one type is better than the other, depending on the detail desired. The chief problem with profilers is that the listening hydrophones are affected by the noise of water moving past them, and this means that ships cannot go at full speed. Considering that ideal speeds for profiling are only 4 to 6 knots, it costs a lot of ship time to obtain the records. We are now conducting experiments which may enable us to go faster and thus do more profiling. These newly developed profilers give records that oceanographers find almost miraculous. In the past, we had to deduce the thickness and structure of sediment in most places from the details of the surface topography as revealed by echo sounders. Now when everything is just right we can see the layers far below the bottom, watch them thicken and thin, and see whether they are flat or have been folded or faulted and then buried. With these marvelous instruments we shall be able to identify places where the sea floor in Melanesia has been deformed recently, where thick undeformed sediment is accumulating, and tell where it is coming from, because the layers usually thicken toward the source.

By measuring the thickness and layering of the crust we hope to establish whether its general character is that of a continent which is being destroyed or an ocean basin which is being built up into a thick continent. This is done by setting off explosions in the ocean and recording the times at which they are detected on a ship or at several floating buoys. There are few precedents to guide us, but that is one reason the region is interesting. The velocity at which explosive-generated waves move through typical continental crust is less than through typical oceanic crust. Consequently, unusually thin continent may not be the same as unusually thick ocean crust. The layering might also differ depending on the history of the upper crust. Thick mud on an old oceanic crust would not resemble the hard sedimentary and metamorphic rocks char-

The sea floor and the crust below as seen with instruments with different power and resolution.

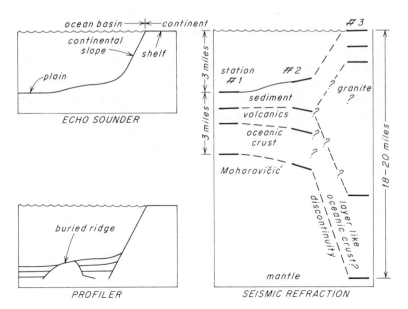

acteristic of the surface of continents. Unfortunately, as my colleague, Al Engel, remarks, "Setting off explosions is not a very sensitive way of analyzing rocks." At least, it will give us a general picture of the structure of the crust which cannot be obtained in any other way.

Variations in the intensity of gravity from place to place result from variations in the thickness and density of the underlying rocks. Geophysicists learn early that gravity observations can be interpreted in an infinite number of ways if nothing else is known. Given the discrete measurements of crustal structure by explosive seismology, however, the interpretation of gravity can be quite informative. The gravity interpretations can be adjusted to agree with the seismic data. This might seem rather pointless and would be if nothing else could be achieved. The value of gravity measurements is that they can be made continuously while the ship is underway between seismic stations, which are limited in number by time and the amount of explosives that the ships can carry. If all goes well and the weather is not too rough for sensitive instruments, we shall have continuous profiles of gravity which can be equated with some confidence to continuous profiles of the crust of Melanesia.

Profiles of magnetic intensity are obtained by towing a magnetometer behind each ship at a distance such that it is unaffected by the steel hull. We shall be seeking the distinctive local magnetic anomalies which have elsewhere demonstrated sea floor spreading. Pre-expedition observations have been made in Melanesia by the U.S. Navy in Project Magnet, using low-flying airplanes. These indicate local magnetic anomalies, which is promising, but flight lines are too few to show whether the anomalies have the characteristic elongate shapes produced by sea floor spreading. If the anomalies are elongate and parallel we shall look for symmetry and centers of spreading. We shall also try to identify the identical sequences of anomalies already found in other places where spreading has occurred. This will give some clues regarding the time of Melanesian spreading. We already have some ideas about where to look for spreading because of the possibility that the large continental islands have drifted. If New Caledonia drifted away from Australia, symmetrical magnetic anomalies may exist in the oceanic crust between them. They may be anticipated for the same reason between Australia and New Zealand. Another likely prospect is that the Lord Howe Rise and Norfolk Ridge are associated in some way with linear magnetic anomalies because they lie in a region with strikingly linear topography. Moreover, New Zealand oceanographers have already shown that the southern part of the Norfolk Ridge has a large positive magnetic anomaly. A last prospect is that the Fiji Plateau is part of a small oceanic rise which is actively spreading and will show typical magnetic anomalies. The evidence is unclear, but the plateau is relatively shallow and has most of the identifying characteristics of an active oceanic rise, so I have great hopes that we shall find it is one.

Heat comes to the surface of the sea floor from deep in the interior of the earth. I do not mean that the abyssal sea floor is warm; on the contrary, it is very close to freezing. But if we plunge a long probe into the bottom sediment and measure the temperature at different points along the probe, we find it is warmer the deeper we go. If we also measure the thermal conductivity of the sediment, we can calculate the flow of heat moving upward from the interior. Were there no complications and if all the heat came from great depth, these measurements would tell us where the mantle is hot and rising and where it is cold and sinking. Such information would be very helpful in trying to establish the origin of the small crustal blocks of Melanesia and whether they are moving. Unfortunately, there are complications. If sediment accumulates rapidly, the heat flow seems low. If a measurement is made on a hill, heat flow seems low and if in a valley, it seems high. Consequently, measurements must be numerous and at carefully selected sites for meaningful interpretation. Existing measurements suggest that heat flow is relatively normal in northwestern Melanesia and relatively high elsewhere in the region. It remains to be seen if these relationships are still true when we have a hundred measurements instead of twenty. If there are centers of sea floor spreading, we may expect to find that heat flow is high along the center line. If the Lord Howe Rise is a part of Melantis it should have normal continental heat flow; if it is an ancient oceanic rise, heat flow may be low.

Having examined the sea floor with every type of modern instrument, we can also fall back on the oldest method of doing geology, namely, taking samples. We do this in several ways: by photographs, cores of sediment, and dredge hauls of rock. Modern deep sea cameras can be located accurately a few meters above the bottom and can take several hundred pictures as the ship drifts along. The photos are developed immediately and provide a guide for other types of sampling. By themselves they show such things as whether ocean currents are intense at the bottom; whether animals and animal borings are abundant; and whether the bottom is paved with nodules of manganese oxide or phosphorite, which are minerals of potential economic importance. Cores are a few inches in diameter and three to thirty feet long. Heavy weights propel the coring pipes vertically into the bottom so the cores show not only the surface sediments but also the layers just below. Sediment accumulates slowly in the ocean, and may not accumulate at all on small hills. Consequently, even these short cores may recover sediment millions of years old. With our profilers we can follow deep layers to places where they reach the surface, on a cliff for example. When we core such a place, we are able to deliberately sample old sediment which we would be very lucky to hit if we did not have profiler records. This is also true for dredge hauls of rock. We used to try to dredge rock from cliffs which often turned out to be covered with mud. Now our chances are better. If our dredging is successful, we should have no difficulty in resolving the nature of the submarine rises and ridges in Melanesia. Continental rocks are strikingly different from those of the ocean basins. If they contain fossils or are fresh enough for radioactive mineral dating, we can also tell their age and a great deal about their history. If they are very old or otherwise unusual, we shall want to make more dredge hauls.

When the expedition was first planned we had the choice of trying to do all these things at once or doing them in stages. We elected the latter course because so many programs are dependent on others. *Horizon* will spend three months sounding and profiling and measuring the magnetic field without ever stopping except twice for fuel. This will give us the information to plan all the subsequent work in following months. We expect to analyze all the data as rapidly as they accumulate, which will require a newly developed method of computer handling. If it works, all the preliminary analysis and much of the final analysis of all the millions of observations will be completed by the time the ships return to San Diego. I certainly hope so, not only because it is essential for planning the later parts of the expedition but also because I shall not go to sea again until it is done. American oceanographic laboratories are loaded with undigested observations, and I do not want to be guilty of adding to the pile.

april, may, june 1967
CHAPTER FIVE

# *At Sea at Last*

**CHAPTER FIVE**  After many a trial, adjustment, compromise, and improvement, April has arrived and the *Nova* Expedition is ready to begin. Or is it? The outstanding problems are concerned with equipment, chiefly magnetometers and profilers. We have been towing magnetometers for years and have a sizable array of equipment, both recorders, which are in the ship's laboratory, and "fish" which are towed behind and contain the sensors. However, in the last few months we have met with a series of disasters. The "fish" look like fish to sharks, and it is not uncommon to find them imbedded with teeth when they are hauled back on the ship. Occasionally a shark also bites the long cable leading to the fish. Perhaps something of the sort happened when we lost one fish west of Mexico. A more common problem is that inexperienced scientists have unjustified faith in the reliability of winches and other ship equipment. Consequently, they do not take steps to avoid improbable misadventures and accidents. The experienced oceanographer takes precautions to avoid any conceivable equipment misbehavior and expects that highly improbable events will surely occur. One time the power lead to the main dredging winch on one of our ships was being repaired in the engine room. No one was near the winch, and a colleague and I were leaning against the after rail awaiting developments. We were directly on a line between the dredge on the deck and the sheave on the end of a boom through which the dredging wire led to the winch. I remarked, "Max, no one is near that winch, and I don't see how it can start. However, if it does, the dredge will be pulled across the deck, pin us against the rail, tear it away, knock us over the side, get jammed against the sheave, break the cable, and fall on top of us in the water. It seems to me that the view is just as good six feet over there where we are not on a line with the winch." We idly moved over, exchanging sea stories. A moment later, the winch started to haul in even though no one was near it. The dredge moved across the deck, tore away the railing, jammed in the sheave, the wire broke, and the dredge disappeared into the deep. We stared at these nearby and dramatic events with some amazement. Shortly, the winch operator climbed out of a hatch leading up from the engine room and after stopping the winch explained that he had shorted some wires down below.

The improbable events that lose magnetometer fish are connected with the apparatus for hauling them back on board. Something went wrong on an expedition off Mexico at this time and another fish went into the deep. Meanwhile, on land a far more unlikely event occurred. The magnetometer recorders are trays of electronic gear in a light steel rack. A technician put two recorders in the back of a truck and failed to lash them in place because he was moving them only to a nearby building. He went over a small bump and they fell to the road, a distance of six feet which turned out to be just far enough for complete demolition. Suddenly, our collection of instruments was beginning to look a little sparse. There was a further problem in that they are homemade, because commercial ones did not meet our requirements when they were built. Consequently, they can be maintained only by people with special training or experience. This was not expected to be a problem because the best instruments require only minimum maintenance. However, they are now gone, and we can see repair problems looming. We have electronics technicians on the ships, but they are not familiar with the magnetometers and there is no time to train them. Qualified scientists or technicians will be on some expedition legs; we planned to have them make repairs while aboard. Now it looks as if repairs may be frequent. What to do? We hold conferences. First, the scientists most interested in magnetic measurements, who built the instruments but themselves will not be involved in the early legs, very generously agree to put the best instruments on the ships. This leaves them with only parts of old equipment for their own work in the spring. However, they take the gallant attitude that if they cannot build new equipment then they deserve what happens to them.

Thus *Horizon* goes to sea with the best equipment available and the second best as a standby. It works perfectly at the dock in the hands of experienced technicians. For the next two months it never works again while the ship is in use for work unconnected with *Nova*. Clearly, we have to do something before starting *Nova* from Kwajalein Atoll where we take over *Horizon*. The best scheme is to fly an expert to Kwajalein to make new repairs and also familiarize the *Nova* scientists with the equipment. In early April, Tom Chase and the *Nova* party leave San Diego for Kwajalein accompanied by a technician to fix the instruments. They are operational when he flies back, but will they remain so at sea?

Scripps has a radio station to communicate with our far-flung fleet. We exchange radio messages as easily as inter-office memoranda. *Horizon* sails on 8 April and Chase's first message comes on the 11th. "Streaming well. Mag working so far. Top speed with arcer during test was 5.5 knots." The magnetometer (mag) problem is temporarily solved, at least, and we have more time to worry about our second equipment problem—the speed at which we can obtain suitable records towing a profiler. These instruments are always being improved and made more powerful until it becomes easy to get the good records needed to solve some problem. Then, if they are working just right, it develops that they can just barely obtain records usable to solve some previously intractable problem. Consequently, at any given time the profilers may or may not be easy to use, depending on whether they are being used to solve the problem for which they were designed or the next more difficult one for which they are inadequate. Our present models work well at fast ship speeds in shallow water or at slow speeds in deep water but not both. Naturally, on *Nova* we want to go fast in deep water. Tom Chase's first message indicates that he can get good records only at speeds half as great as normal cruising speed. Consequently, he can go only half as far in the time allotted to the first leg. The profiler and other records have to be obtained in the right places during the reconnaissance phase of *Nova*, and so he will be making complicated tentative schedules trying to save time. He will slow to profile where it looks most worthwhile and speed up to collect other records and make up distance where he can.

Subsequent radio messages indicate all is well. By 15 April, Chase has profiled across the northern margin of Melanesia and crossed a drowned atoll which has a thick fill of sediment under the lagoon. By the 22nd he has twice crossed the Fiji Plateau and reports thin sediment. This discovery makes profiling of little value and he saves time by doing it intermittently. On the 24th comes a request for some spare parts to be forwarded to Brisbane. Also a request for ink. This latter shows how accustomed we are to operating in remote regions. We suggest that they just buy the ink in Brisbane. The last message in April indicates all is still well, and moreover the Norfolk Ridge and Lord Howe Rise are covered with thick sediment and the flat tops are not caused by erosion at a former sea level. This is the first obvious discovery that will affect planning of the later phases of the expedition.

On the first of May troubles begin anew. A morning message indicates that the magnetometer is giving trouble. Six minutes later the question of repairs in Brisbane is raised because neither mag is working ideally. We have some more conferences. We cannot send a technician to Brisbane because the ship would be delayed while waiting for him and in this phase profiler records are more important than magnetic ones. The choices open are to hire commercial repairs in Brisbane, lease a mag somewhere in the world and fly it to Brisbane, or buy a new one and fly it down. I send a message authorizing commercial repair if obtainable. We can get delivery on a leased mag from California and later apply part of the leasing cost to purchase if we want. However, the instrument avail-

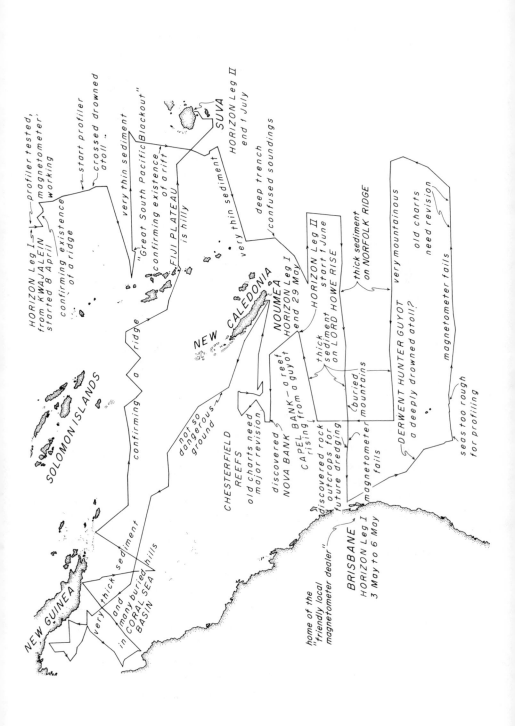

NEW GUINEA

very thick sediment and many buried hills in CORAL SEA BASIN

SOLOMON ISLANDS

confirming a ridge

not so dangerous ground

CHESTERFIELD REEFS
old charts need major revision

discovered NOVA BANK

CAPEL BANK – a reef rising from a guyot

discovered rock outcrops for future dredging

NEW CALEDONIA

NOUMEA
HORIZON Leg I
end 29 May

HORIZON Leg I
from KWAJALEIN
started 8 April

profiler tested, magnetometer working

confirming existence of a ridge

start profiler

crossed drowned atoll

very thin sediment

"Great South Pacific Blackout"

confirming existence of a rift

FIJI PLATEAU
is hilly

very thin sediment

SUVA

HORIZON Leg II
end 1 July

deep trench

confused soundings

HORIZON Leg II
start 1 June

thick sediment on LORD HOWE RISE

thick sediment on NORFOLK RIDGE

buried mountains

magnetometer fails

DERWENT HUNTER GUYOT
a deeply drowned atoll?

very mountainous

old charts need revision

magnetometer fails

seas too rough for profiling

home of the "friendly local magnetometer dealer"

BRISBANE
HORIZON Leg I
3 May to 6 May

able is not the latest model. Such a model will be available for delivery in a month when *Horizon* stops in Noumea. After considering the urgency of other requests from Scripps scientists for expensive equipment, Associate Director Fred Spiess authorizes spending $20,000 for a new commerical magnetometer and the problem is as solved as it can be. Tom Chase leaves the ship at Brisbane and Stuart Smith follows him as chief scientist. I cable Stu to keep trying with the mags on hand and that a new one will arrive at Noumea.

It will cost $1000 to ship the mag by air and many hundreds more to forward spare parts for other equipment. It seems disgraceful to be involved with wasteful emergency measures, but we are trapped. I like to run a nice tidy expedition with the latest reliable equipment and spares for the spares, but so do all oceanographers, and there is not enough money to go around.

We leave Stu Smith ready to sail from Brisbane, and return to *Argo*, which starts on the *Nova* Expedition from San Diego on 17 April. Under Chief Scientist Ed Goldberg, the ship will go to Pago Pago with a few stops for stations to collect air, water, and sediment samples. There are two magnetometers aboard and, Joy!, a highly qualified technician to maintain them. George Shor has become so concerned with the loss of ship time from slow speeds while profiling that he decides to go along and experiment to see what can be done to improve things. A few days before sailing time, Shawn Biehler from M.I.T. arrives to study our shipborne gravimeter. Until he decided to go on *Nova*, we had no one really interested in Melanesian gravity measurements. Experience shows that we rarely get first-class records unless the scientist who will eventually study them is on board the collecting ship or at least personally involved in the expedition. He brings welcome news—he is ordering a new magnetometer and will fly it to join *Argo* in Hawaii in June. We shall have more reserves. He also has a new type of gravimeter under development, and with luck he will bring it when he joins the ship at Suva in July. His type is expected to work in rougher seas than our model and thus might give more measurements. When I take Biehler to see the ship for the first time he finds it chaotic with wires, equipment, and supplies being loaded everywhere. It looks highly organized to me and I compliment the Captain and scientists for having the preparations for sailing so well in hand.

Off they go on 17 April, sailing half a mile to the fuel dock to load Shor's explosives, and then into the Pacific. Next stop Pago Pago? As it develops, it is Midway Atoll, several thousand miles to the north. Shor has the air-gun type of profiler working at 9 knots, which is already an improvement over the best we can do on *Horizon* with the arcer type. However, he is having trouble with the recorder part of the instrument and calls for Alan Jones to fly out to Midway to help. Fortunately, only a few hours of ship time are needed to pick up Jones because the ship is going near Midway anyway. The first message after leaving Midway indicates that *Argo* is profiling at 11.5 knots and getting very peculiar records. The top thousand feet of sediment are almost transparent to sound waves and can hardly be distinguished from the overlying water. This phenomenon has been reported by oceanographers from Lamont Geological Observatory but is new to us. The first leg for *Argo* seems a complete success except for a series of messages indicating that one of the oceanographic winches needs spare parts, which can be delivered to Hawaii for pickup in June. Shor and Goldberg fly home from Pago Pago and turn the ship over to Bill Van Dorn, who will return it to us in Hawaii after completing work unrelated to *Nova*.

Meanwhile, Tom Chase has flown in from Brisbane bearing loads of absolutely fascinating records from the first leg of *Horizon*. At last, some results in hand after so many months of planning and preparation. It is immediately apparent that Chase and party have done a superb job at sea. All the different types of records have been plotted on composite profiles and everything is ready for analysis. We start to study the records and speculate about their meaning, but not much can be said until the second month of the reconnaissance is completed.

Stuart Smith is chief scientist on *Horizon* on the leg from Brisbane to Noumea. His first radio message on 11 May is modestly encouraging in that the magnetometer is working again, but the seas have become so rough that the profiler cannot penetrate the bottom sediment. He reports an intriguing observation that Derwent Hunter guyot has the shape of a drowned atoll even though it is at a depth of about 1000 feet. If so, it is the deepest former atoll known and may have subsided very rapidly. Stu continues to report at frequent intervals. The mag soon collapses for the last time. However, profiling is working very well with deep penetration, and thick sediment is turning up everywhere. A new problem arises—how to run the ship through an area of almost continuous reefs —but is solved on the spot by the usual technique of traveling with the sun to avoid reflections which might conceal shoals. *Horizon* emerges from the reefs and reaches Noumea, where Stu and others fly home and Jerry Winterer begins his work in the Coral Sea. Before he leaves he radios that the magnetometer which we shipped at enormous expense is stranded in Auckland, and will I make sure it gets to Suva?

Enough is enough. At the recommendation of Pan American World Airlines we shipped the magnetometer on a plane that went to Sydney, refueled, and then flew to Noumea. That way, they said, we need not worry about anything getting lost, as it might be if the gear were transferred from one plane to another at Suva. Then they offload everything in Auckland and let it sit. The character of messages we then send to Pan Am becomes a little less friendly, until our agent at last reports that the shipment is in hand in Suva.

Stu returns with a splendid nautical beard and another month of beautiful records. Combining the work of *Argo* and *Horizon* during this reconnaissance phase, we already are on the track of several fascinating problems. The first of these is concerned with the structure and submergence of atolls and guyots—the problem that intrigued Charles Darwin more than a century ago. When guyots were first discovered, it seemed possible that they were capped with a frosting of sedimentary ooze and that this capping made them flat. Subsequent dredging and sounding proved that in most places the capping is thin or absent and the flat tops are caused by truncation by waves when the guyots were once higher. On *Nova* George Shor made profiler crossings of two guyots in the central Pacific and found a capping roughly a thousand feet thick in the center. Under the capping can be seen the partially truncated top of the old volcano, but the guyot clearly is so flat only because sediment has buried irregular rock. The guyots in this region were islands 60 million to 100 million years ago, and presumably the sediment capping has been accumulating ever since they first sank. Thus the whole geological history of the sinking may be contained in the sedimentary layers which are at a shallow depth where we can get at them.

In the Melanesian region *Horizon* crossed some other guyots and drowned atolls and also found something new. It appears that the region has been elevated and depressed much more than we had reason to believe before.

Most of what we have learned is about the Lord Howe Rise and Norfolk Ridge because we have six profiles across them. The Lord Howe Rise is really a series of parallel mountain ranges running north-south. The easternmost is in many ways the most interesting, because it is very smooth and rounded to the south and grows steadily hillier to the north. The smoothness results from a thick capping of sediment, and the basement rocks beneath the sediment are quite irregular everywhere. The next mountain range west is lower and very hilly but also has a thick covering of sediment over irregular basement. To the north the range includes several high, although submerged, volcanoes with a frosting of coral. At about 20° north latitude the frosting has completely covered all sea floor mountains, and reefs are continuous in a large area. The westernmost of the Lord Howe mountain ranges is a line of extinct volcanoes which were once islands but are now guyots and atolls. Thus, the shape of the sea floor was once very different from what it is now. What is the meaning of these depth changes? Why are these mountains buried under such thick sediment, and why is it smoothest to the south? These are puzzles for the next stages of the expedition.

The Norfolk Ridge is only the westernmost of a group of mountain ranges like those of the Lord Howe Rise. Indeed, they seem very similar except they are deeper and do not have a thick blanket of sediment. Are they deeper only because they lack sediment? It certainly appears so. But why is one group of mountains covered with sediment and not the other?

We left Jerry Winterer and party on the way to the Coral Sea on *Horizon*. His radio messages are full of good news. The ship passes through the "dangerous ground" of the Chesterfield Island reefs without incident and arcs the length of the Coral Sea Basin. The sea floor in the basin is completely flat because most hills have been buried under 3000 feet or more of sediment. However, a few basement hills protrude through the mud and sand. *Horizon* zigzags toward New Guinea and then reverses course on the long run toward Suva, where she is due on 1 July.

*Argo* heads toward the same goal. Harmon Craig and most of the graduate students fly to Honolulu, load explosives, and head west. Craig's first message is chilling. He has found that the magnetometer was towed too close to the steel ship for the first two months and we shall have to apply suitable corrections to all the data. These are the times that try men's patience. Why, you ask yourself, does the National Science Foundation give money to a bunch of knuckleheads who can't even run a magnetometer? Do they always bumble along like this, breaking equipment, flying technicians across the Pacific to make repairs, shipping replacements to the wrong ports? Well, the arcer and the air-gun and the echo sounders have been working beautifully and even the magnetometers have worked most of the time. And the ships keep going, which is something of an achievement in itself, considering that *Horizon* is ready for the scrap yard after this cruise, and *Argo* is not far from it. Our troubles would have been but wisps of air if a little more money and a little less improvisation had gone into the expedition.

Professors like to talk. With students aboard we like to keep things lively because we hope they too will learn to love work at sea. Consequently, the radio traffic begins to get livelier. A few days after the ship leaves Honolulu, I think the students might be feeling under the weather and like some reference to land. Information about our coming field trip in New Zealand should be just the thing. I radio "Bradley has planned exciting field trip. Fly over White Island to Rotorua. Bus around thermal area and Taupo. Return by bus to Auckland through graywackes. Start 13 September return 16. Stay

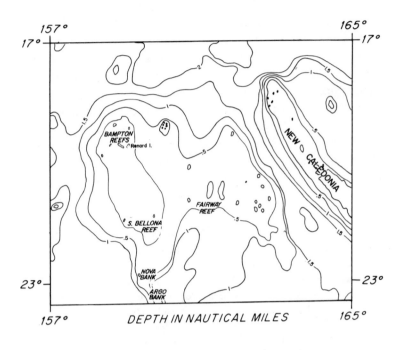

DEPTH IN NAUTICAL MILES

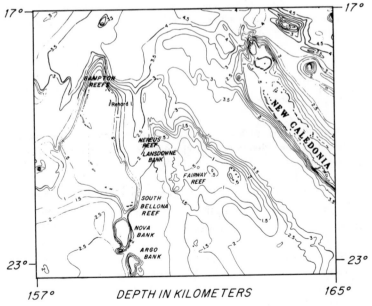

DEPTH IN KILOMETERS

Redoing the map. Above, the "dangerous ground" before *Nova*; below, after *Nova*.

in municipal motel. All sounds great. Am confirming arrangements with him. Please inform students of prospect." Craig
radios back not long after, "Students all doing well. Active
seminar program; students on programs, crew members on
seamanship. Good weather, high spirits." He also indicates
that sediment cores and heat flow measurements had been
made successfully and the other programs are under way.

On this leg of *Nova*, *Argo* will cross the equator, and this
calls for initiation of polliwogs by shellbacks according to the
ancient rite of the sea. However, the rite has changed in the
course of time, and I think it only appropriate to practice
scholarship on a university ship. Consequently, I radio Craig
how it had been done on *Endeavour* during Captain Cook's
first voyage, as reported in the Journal of Sir Joseph Banks.

> Banks Endeavour Journal provides useful precedent for scientific
> ship crossing the line. Quote. Captn Cook and Doctor Solander
> were on the black list as were myself, my servants, and dogs
> which I was obliged to compound for by giving the duckers a cer-
> tain quantity of brandy for which they willingly excused us the
> ceremony. Many of the men, however, chose to be duckd rather
> than give up 4 days allowance of wine which was the price fixd
> upon and, of course, all the boys were ducked.

This serves the double purpose of reminding the students
that they will be ducked and reaffirming that some famous
scientists cannot spell. Craig replies:

> Students agree giving up 4 days rum rations as soon as you
> initiate same. Please advife where stored and authorize disburs-
> ment soonest.

This was followed by a long message describing the discovery of two enormous extinct submarine volcanoes and the
problem of naming them. In abstract,

> Discovered two magnificent seamounts 53 miles apart with almoft
> identical size and profile.... Proposed names are Dixon Seamount
> and Dixon Bif. Dixon conspicuously absent in sack during furvey.
> Disdains names.

To both of which I replied, in abstract again,

> Old sea dog Dixon is right. Improper to name seamounts after all
> or part of any living oceanographer involved in expedition. Are
> you all talking the language of Doctor Johnson? Your messages
> consistently replace "S" with "F." Rum is in usual place.

The ships, of course, or unfortunately, are dry.

The final preparations for the next leg on *Horizon* are
now in train. All twenty-four items on my checklist of charts
and replacement parts are safely packed to take to the airport.
All fifteen items on my checklist of mortgage payments, bank
deposits, taxes, and the like while I am away are now the
problems of my wife. All fifty-six items in the list of things I
have to do in order to leave my office for three months are
crossed out. I have tickets, passport, vaccination record, money,
and a note telling me where I am going. All I need to do before flying to Suva to join *Horizon* is post a Xerox copy of the
opening page of *Moby Dick* on my office door:

> Whenever I find myself growing grim about the mouth; whenever
> it is damp, drizzly November in my soul; whenever I find myself
> involuntarily pausing before coffin warehouses, and bringing up
> the rear of every funeral I meet; and especially whenever my
> hypos get such an upper hand of me, that it requires a strong
> moral principle to prevent me from deliberately stepping into the
> street, and methodically knocking people's hats off—then I account
> it high time to get to sea as soon as I can. This is my substitute
> for pistol and ball. With a philosophical flourish Cato throws him-
> self upon his sword; I quietly take to the ship. There is nothing
> surprising in this. If they but knew it, almost all men in their
> degree, some time or other, cherish very nearly the same feelings
> towards the ocean with me.

# The Ship HORIZON

**CHAPTER SIX** And so June 29th, up at 6, off to the airport, unload 210 pounds of books, extra diamond drills, spare electronics parts, rolls of just-completed charts and a few clothes, and wait. Coffee and cigarette—no breakfast today. Ned Allison arrives, discuss baggage weight problem, wait. George Hohnhaus arrives, discuss baggage, wait. Warren Smith arrives. Check in for flight, splitting extra bags between us. Check bags only to San Francisco; cannot risk another misadventure like the magnetometer shipment to Noumea. In the air, discuss plans and changes in ship rigging with Hohnhaus. More coffee, no food.

Into San Francisco. Collect baggage and haul to Qantas. Teddy Bullard arrives, having flown in from London. Qantas very reasonable about excess baggage. Charged in the curious units of £2 per kilogram. On to Honolulu where Clem Chase and Dave Johnson meet plane. Party now assembled. Whole process invokes memory of opening scenes in *High Noon*. Unexpected addition, Terry Hansen, replacement captain for *Horizon*, also climbs on plane. After sixteen hours under way, approach Nadi airport in Fiji. Immigration official will not admit several of us because we have no tickets showing departure from Fiji. Explain we have own ship; does not matter. Suggest that Hansen and I write tickets for a voyage on *Horizon*; not well received. Suggest that we buy tickets for return to Honolulu using air credit cards, pass through immigration, and then cancel tickets. A winner. Bureaucrats happy, we are happy, Qantas ticket clerk resigned to a little paperwork.

Up at 0520 to catch flight to Suva. Crazy schedules in the southwestern Pacific. Have now stayed twice in the Skylodge near the airport and never had a chance to see it in daylight. *Horizon* not in port when we fly over but is docked by the time we arrive by cab from the airport. Off to the hotel to clean up while the ship clears customs and immigration and then on board at last. Jerry Winterer, Pat Wilde, and the others are in good spirits. Most of the equipment worked most of the time, and I have the pleasure of seeing results all plotted and ready for the next stage of the operations. Winterer and I immediately begin to discuss results and to plan.

From the 1st to the 4th of July the ship remains in port awaiting supplies and overhaul of some engine parts. On the third I move on the ship to speed up preparations by putting in a constant presence. Everyone is cooperative, but nothing seems to be happening. We are at the mercy of shore facilities in which people seem to have mastered the tea break before learning how to work. I spend my time reorganizing the laboratory, magazine, and chart supplies and becoming reacquainted or acquainted with the officers and crew. The laboratory shows all the stigmata of constant use during the early legs of *Nova*. When it leaves port the ship's laboratory is full of gear but looks as homey as a motel room. After a while the occupants reveal themselves, their feelings, and their work. Mostly this is achieved with masking tape, which will hold paper to damp surfaces in the tropics.

This lab has lots of notices taped up:

1. **A notice to scientific watch standers about annotating the echo sounder records, and a similar notice about profiler records**
2. **A notice that the magnetometer stopped working at a time some months back**
3. **A notice that the last profiler run ended 2247 hours on 23 June (This is stuck on the profiler recorder to identify the number of the next profiler record, which may not be made for some time)**
4. **An envelope taped on the wall and labeled "key to arcer doghouse" which will not be opened until the next profiler run**

5. A large greeting card, "Best wishes for a happy trip," by Emett

6. Various tables and graphs enabling the reader to convert fathoms to meters, local time to San Diego or Greenwich time, revolutions of the propeller drive shaft to ship speed through the water, and the load on the dredging cable as a function of wire angle

7. A splendid collection of homemade Rorschach tests which, it later developed, were posted to mystify the ship's physician who had taken to psychoanalyzing the crew

8. A Xerox copy of a map of variations in intensity of the earth's magnetic field

9. A weekly calendar twelve days out of date, presumably because the scientific watches pay no attention to the day of the week

10. A diagram drawn on a paper towel in two colors showing how to operate a particular three-position switch

11. A Xerox copy of a profiler record taken by a sister institution in the Melanesian region and labeled "Not for Publication" by me when I received it

12. A cartoon showing the Atlantic Ocean being created by two demons who are pushing Africa and South America apart

13. A notice "do not disturb: delicate, scientific instrument in operation" adjacent to a nail swinging as a pendulum on a string attached to a wooden partition lying athwartships. The depth of the groove worn as the ship rolls past the nail indicates frequent rolls to 15° and enough to 30° to leave a mark

14. A canoe paddle hangs from the ceiling and its markings show that the expedition is endorsed by GMC which stands for Geological Moving Consultants, an organization my associates created after one of our many shifts of office furniture

15. A cartoon labeled "NOVA" and showing a five-legged beast with an arcing tail

16. A color postcard of marching sabras with slung burp guns labeled "Women of Israeli Army" and mailed from Tel Aviv some months earlier. It apparently was taped on the wall during the Israeli-Arab war which began and ended while the ship was at sea on Leg II of *Nova*.

Sprinkled among the notices are the fourteen instruments and recorders which make this a laboratory instead of anything else. They sense various characteristics of the environment around the ship, of the operations of the ship under way, and of the winches and wires when the ship is stopped.

What is it like, this ship *Horizon*? According to a brass

plaque she is Hull 347, built by Levingston Shipbuilding Company, Orange, Texas, 1944. She is 143 feet long, 33 feet wide, and draws 13 to 16 feet depending on her load. She displaces about 800 tons, or somewhat less than the Manila galleons of the sixteenth century but more than the *Endeavour*, in which Captain Cook sailed. *Horizon* was the first deep sea ship acquired by Scripps, in 1949, and I have been sailing on her from time to time ever since. She has always been a happy ship, and I have often wondered what subtle difference in design from her sister ship *Baird* caused one to be happy and the other not. *Horizon* has sailed around the world and been to every part of the Pacific. I do not know how far she has gone, but I have no reservations in saying that Levingston Shipbuilding Company can be proud of her.

*Horizon* is not without flaw. Now and then the main engines, one or both, break down, but somehow they give the impression of doing the best they can. At Suva one engine is in fairly good shape, but the other has had over 9000 hours of use since the last complete overhaul. The next such overhaul is due at 10,000 hours and the ship is 2000 hours from San Diego. I suppose that at some time both engines will collapse at once and we shall again have what we occasionally call a "half-day floatabout" or what appears on the records of Leg I of *Nova* as "The Great South Pacific Blackout." Our students usually have difficulty in believing that oceanographic ships break down. Ours certainly do.

What of the men who run and use this ship? She normally has a crew of eighteen or nineteen and anywhere from three to seventeen scientists, students, and technicians. The scientific party leaving from Suva will be thirteen and include five professors, a senior research scientist, six students, and one technician. The party includes residents of France, England, and Australia, and students or professors from four universities. They are a typical academic research group in all respects except that they like to go to sea or at the very least are interested in the oceans.

These special qualities they share with the crew but otherwise the groups are relatively distinct. The crew in general were once in the Navy and have retired or else come from the fishing fleet or, in smaller numbers, from the merchant marine. Several of the senior deck officers and engineers have spent their entire careers with Scripps. Each cruise new faces appear, but usually among the seamen and oilers, who have the least training and pay. Most of the crew tend to ship over, in Navy parlance, which is an interesting point considering that as University employees, they are paid less per hour than American merchant marine sailors and they live in much more wretched quarters. I think that two factors are of prime importance: first, the work is interesting, and second, it is regular.

The captain of an oceanographic ship has a particularly trying time. Captains, as is well known, legally and in many other ways are lords of all they survey in their ships. This has not always been so. Indeed, only a few hundred years ago the present position of captain other than in a warship would have been that of "master" or "sailing master." The former term is still in use in the merchant marine. Its original connotation, however, has vanished. A "master" was a navigator and later a moving-hotel manager for the chief official on a ship who represented the owners in trading in port. Likewise in the navies of previous centuries the chief official on a ship was a gentleman or army officer rather than the senior man concerned with operating a ship. The authority of the officers of the ship was limited to the affairs necessary to operating it safely and moving it from one desired point to another.

This is essentially the role of the officers and crew aboard an oceanographic research vessel. The realization of this fact requires a great readjustment in attitude among new deck officers and particularly new captains in the Scripps fleet. Adjustment is especially difficult, sometimes impossible, for ex-naval officers who cannot bring themselves to believe that some graduate student on his first marine expedition can call on the intercom from the laboratory to the bridge and direct the ship to stop, turn, or anything else that does not affect its safety. Even ex-merchant marine officers begin with a vague sort of feeling that it should be possible for the scientists to say what they are going to do during the night so the captain can issue his night orders which will be followed without variation by the crew. Oh, the shock of reality. As I said, the captain of an oceanographic research ship has a trying time, but most of them seem to like the work.

Concerned as they are with scientific problems, the scientists and more particularly students sometimes tend to ignore the crew when all is well and complain when it isn't. This would be insufferable if the crew were helpless, but happily they react with spirit. For example, some people are sensitive about titles. The "chief scientist" on our expeditions used to be called the "expedition leader" and sometimes still is. The crew on one ship took to calling this individual the "cruise director," which does not sound very different but is a title normally reserved for the person who keeps track of the games schedules on a passenger liner. This gentle and imaginative mutiny is reported to have had some effect.

In general, scientists and crew get along on a basis of mutual need. Without the scientists' ideas there would be no need for the ships and no jobs. Without crews' skills the ships would not sail and the ideas could not be tested. Among the crew and scientists who have sailed together there is also a feeling of mutual respect based on shared experience and demonstrated ability to muddle through.

What of life aboard the ship? I am typing this sentence on the ship sailing at 11.3 knots in the open sea, and it is a tribute to the Smith-Corona model 250 electric typewriter that it is possible. The reason is that the ship is constantly in motion. The possible motions of a ship are forward and backward, up and down, and sideways, with the related seesawing motions of pitching, rolling, and yawing. Some of the infinite combinations and permutations of these basic motions are sufficiently distinctive to deserve special names such as lurch, porpoise, and sink. *Horizon* does everything but sink. The ship moves. The contents move. The ship and contents periodically intersect, resulting in broken pencil points, spilled jam, or bruises, depending on the contents involved.

Sleeping presents problems. Even staying in a bunk sometimes presents problems. If the ship heads directly into a low swell, it sometimes pitches without other complicating motions. On these rare occasions one can sleep on his back, being subjected to no more than a gentle motion about like lying in the center of a seesaw while two children work the ends up and down. If the ship rolls, and it usually does, it is impossible to sleep lying on the back because the motion tips one from side to side. The best position is lying about half on the stomach with one elbow and a knee wedged against the side of the bunk.

Eating also requires some modification from normal life. Our meals are acquired cafeteria style from the galley. In very quiet weather one can put a plate on a table and eat, but not so when even an ordinary sea is running. Then it is frequently necessary to hold one edge of a plate and tilt it back and forth to keep the food in place while the ship rolls. A knife cannot be placed on the edge of a plate because it slides off. It stays put if placed in the hollow of a spoon. Likewise, the prudent sailor hooks his fork over the edge of his plate whenever he puts it down.

Other natural functions present similar problems. After a short time on *Horizon* most people are no longer conscious of all the adjusting and balancing they do to stay upright. Thus, it is apt to be a surprise if you are seated, and thus fixed in position, to see a shipmate staggering and lurching down a passageway as though he were roaring drunk. So the water from the drinking fountain or into the urinal appears to behave in defiance of gravity. Visualizing himself as fixed while actually rolling with the ship, the fascinated observer watches a stream of rising or falling water writhe and sway through the air.

Every aspect of work is affected by constant motion. Anything placed on a bench top almost immediately slides off unless it is lashed, nailed, screwed, cleated, or taped into place. All small items in frequent use go into small cardboard boxes taped to walls or the sides of equipment. While reading or annotating the output recordings of instruments it is usually necessary to hold on to something to prevent smashing the knobs and dials. In the lab are two deck chairs in which someone occasionally rests, but not by merely sitting. The chairs must be wedged or braced into a corner or against a wall or the sitter soon becomes a slider or a faller or a flier.

The dredging, coring, and other outside work is done on the fantail, in the stern of the ship. Much of it is only a few feet above the water at the best of times. This is so the equipment can be lowered into the sea and recovered with a minimum chance of crushing it against the side of the ship. This philosophy doubtless is good for equipment, but bad for oceanographers. We hardly ever work on the fantail without getting wet, and consequently we habitually wear shorts and Japanese-style beach sandals made of rubber and with thongs between the toes. This costume is ideal in the hot tropics where the water is pleasantly cooling. It is less enjoyable in the cold waters off northern California which come down from the Aleutian Islands and the Gulf of Alaska. Nevertheless, we hate to wear anything else because the only alternative is heavy rubber boots, socks, and trousers, and it is very trying when the boots become filled with water, as they inevitably do. Soon the ship is full of steaming clothes and stinking boots.

Rocked to starboard, rolled to larboard, such is normal life on the happy *Horizon* and many a similar small oceanographic ship. Unfortunately, mere existence is a little more challenging in a gale in the tropics. As the weather freshens in a gale, the ship begins to creak and groan. Suddenly, a crash echoes through the passageways and something which someone neglected to lash down during good weather is strewn over the deck. Soon the water is green rather than white as it breaks over the rail and sloshes across the fantail. Soon the portholes and then the hatches on the main decks are closed and sea stories are related as old hands point to the high water mark where the deck of the lab was last flooded. Soon curses from the galley show that the cook is gamely trying to make a hot dinner but is beginning to wonder if sandwiches or a cold buffet will be well received. After a day or two everyone is tired and when not on watch spends more and more time in his bunk trying to rest or even sleep. Not much chance. In heavy weather one adopts the *Horizon*-sprawl in bed. Flat on the stomach, wedge the left elbow against the left side of the bunk while simultaneously bracing the right knee against the right side. By then hooking the left foot and the right hand over opposite ends of the mattress, one is ready to sleep in all but the most trying circumstance, i.e., heading into a heavy sea. Then the ship pitches, porpoises, and generally behaves in a manner calculated to cause momentary and quite unjustified doubts as to the reliability of the Texas welders in 1944. A mere nightmare of falling does not compare with the reality of flashing from exhausted sleep into full consciousness that you are suspended in mid-air and that the ship has fallen from under you and is about to hit something. Surely, it is going to be another wave. Who ever heard of an oceanographic ship full of precision echo sounders running into a rock? Think of the disgrace. And then it hits and shudders and rises to the next swell and can it possibly hold together for just one more? The anchor chain begins to stir in the chain locker. Something creaks and something slides in a drawer. Sometimes a drawer falls out, although each has a catch to keep it closed, and the contents are strewn over the deck. Get up and pick up and wedge in place and lash and tape. Another lunge, another crash into the swell; the senior men in the ship live in rooms higher above the water. Most regret it during storms because they are thrown about more than the men in the hold. Moreover, as one of the students who slept in the hold remarked, "In a forward bunk you have the satisfaction of knowing that if the ship runs aground you will be the first man to reach land."

That is life in a gale; in high latitudes, the "roaring for-ties" and "furious fifties," it may continue so without interruption for weeks. The traveler on an ocean liner, the sailor on an oil tanker or an aircraft carrier, cannot imagine what life is like on a small ship. But our scientists return again and again to sea, and our crews, who live on the ships far more than the scientists, look upon our tiny ships as home. Indeed, to a sailor a ship may mean far more than a mere home. During the naval war in Melanesian waters, an American cruiser was sunk and some survivors drifted for days in life rafts. The few who were rescued from one raft reported that many of their mates could not believe that the security of the ship was really gone. Some, crazed by thirst and exposure, thought that they saw the ship peopled as before with shipmates alive and safe under the water, plunged off the raft and drowned trying to return to the protecting steel walls. I like to think that it had been a happy ship.

# Leg III  Uplifted Islands

Completing
a gravity
core.

Oholer     Church    Brenner

The wet laboratory,
an array of
Biere bottles.

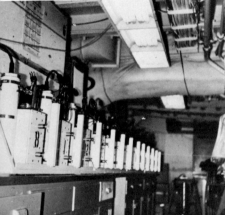

The wet
laboratory,
Bieri!

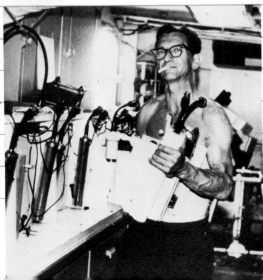

1

Professor Galdberg

The ceremony of crossing the Line.

Allison    Johnson    Smith

Johnhaus

We spent a great deal of time putting the magnetometer fish into the water and then paying out endless kable

3

so that we could record things in the lab

thomas ↑precision recorder for soundings

Carter

and plot them on charts.

Holden

4

Menard

Meanwhile we relaxed inside

and out before hauling in the

Wille

Hohnhaus

magnetometer again in order to stop at the island of

5

Futuna
which is
full of
happy
Polynesia
and
musical
pigs.

6

Bullard          Winterer

M. Aubin welcomed the expedition field party and offered accommodations at one of the new guest houses, a "fale" next to this one.

He also showed them the beauties of the island.

7

Winterer

Later the scientists inspected the interesting features of the elevated modern reef around <u>Futuna</u>.

forme coral head now erode at base

Bullard

allison

wilde

Next day the shipborne dredging party returned to Futuna and studied the pillow lavas which form only underwater and thus have been elevated like the reef.

9

Dahlberg  Bonham  Quig

Then we were underway again and enjoyed delightful weather until

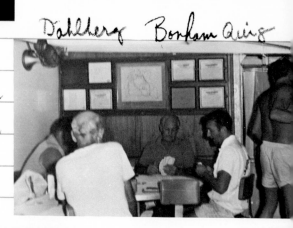

allison
Bullard
Menard
Wilde

Winterer

Johnson

Johnson

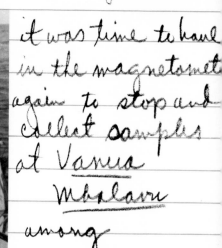

it was time to haul in the magnetomet again to stop and collect samples at Vanua

Mbalavu

among

Carter

the
Exploring
Islands.

Like our
predecessors of
the Challenger
Expedition
a century ago,

Menard     Allison

we climbed
in a boat and
headed ashore.

Smith     Winterer     Bullard

11

It took a little while to get organized but eventually we hired two boats and boatmen and bearers and went off to collect samples of fossil limestone and more of the uplifted pillow lava which solidified under water.

Wilder

Bullard    Winterer

Johnson   Winterer  Bullard

During two days we did a great deal of wading to and from the boats. Finally we reassembled on the

Holden

beach to await arrival of the ship. While it was anchored, the bottom sediment of the lagoon was sampled with low-cost equipment. Next we sailed overnight to Suva

← Wilde

13

Larson

Weiss

Francheteau

Sclater

Slawson

The Horizon and Argo were
together for the first time during the
Expedition, so we had a party at the
Grand Pacific Hotel.

Hohnhaus

ater
homas
enhouse

greenhouse
Clater

When we left <u>Suva</u> at the start of Leg IV the main heat flow program began. This involved preparing the wire, then putting the spear-like probe over and turning the pinger, a self-contained echo sounder, before attaching it to the same wire 300 ft above the probe.

WIRE

ECHO FROM PINGER

PINGER

PROBE

Abranson

thomas
Hohnhaus

15

After leaving a shore
party to sample the
island of Rotuma,
we started to survey
and dredge the
Fiji Plateau.

Smith Allison Gibson Bullard

Chase

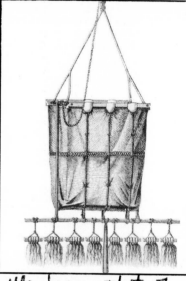

Our dredge differs little from that of
the Challenger.

Ours uses more
steel but it
still breaks
sometimes.

thomas   Johnson  Hohnhaus

(Sir) John Murray?

Consequently we are happy when it brings something up.
We sift the deposit just about as they did on Challenger but, although the British have lost none of their style, some American oceanographer do not seem to have grasped how to work on a ship.

Branson

rof.
Ellison

Sir Edward Bullard disembarking at Lautoka

17

From Lautoka to Noumea the seas
were generally rough but we surveyed,
dredged, and measured heat flow
when we could.

18

At Noumea I moved to Argo. The laboratory on Challenger a century ago was larger than on Argo. However our laboratory has air conditioning to coddle all the electronics gear.

Smith

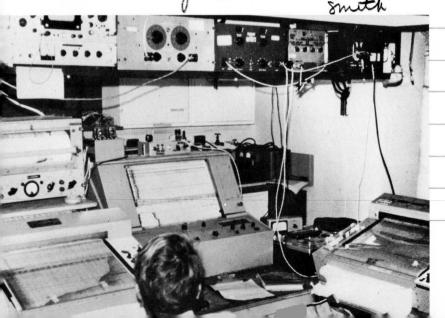

(1)

On a seismic station the explosive charges are small when the ships are close together (1) but get bigger as the shooting ship moves away (2). Then the shooters stop and the listening ship becomes the shooter and vice versa (3).

newhouse on argo

(2)

C. Chase    (3)    abranson on Horizon

Hohnhaus

20

Dixon Oboler Summerhays Solomon

Francheteau

While the ship is stopped to listen, we also take cores or photographs of the sea floor, or measure heat flow.

Bell    Francheteau

As the instruments go up and down for miles through the deep ocean, the scientists can relax.

Summerhays    Oboler

21

the length of the
hydrophone
cables often need
adjusting in
order to
listen better to
Explosions!

Kirk

Women now occupy a more central role
in shipboard oceanography than they
apparently did in the days of the _Challenger_

22

Walpole Island, our faithful radar beacon.

The sea seems very empty when we pass a deserted island but downright crowded when Argo and Horizon rendezvous to exchange seismic records as we did after the first few seismic stations.

People on the two ships photograph each other and shout friendly insults as though they had been separated for months instead of days.

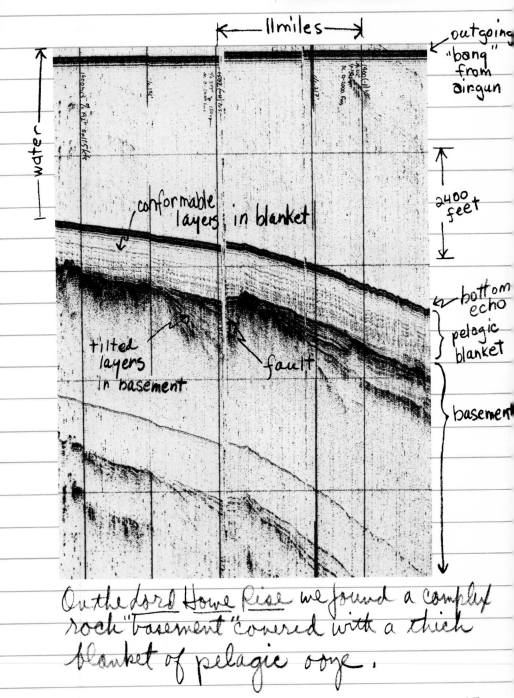

← 11 miles →

outgoing
"bong"
from
airgun

water

conformable
layers in blanket

2400
feet

bottom
echo

pelagic
blanket

tilted
layers
in basement

fault

basement

On the Lord Howe Rise we found a complex
rock "basement" covered with a thick
blanket of pelagic ooze.

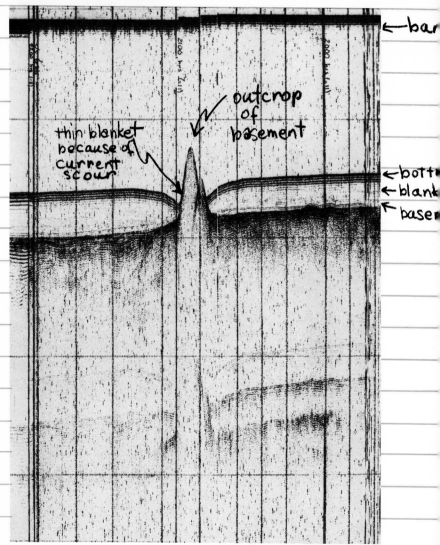

thin blanket
because of
current
scour

outcrop
of
basement

← bar

← bott
← blank
← basem

During the northern seismic station on the Lord Howe Rise, *Argo* crossed an outcrop of basement protruding through the sediment blanket but could not stop to sample it during the shooting run. Unfortunately,

by the end of the run the weather
was too rough for sampling. It stayed
stormy most of the time for the next few
weeks and we were driven into Brisbane

for repairs.

It was stormy
soon after we
returned to
sea.

At last the weather cleared

October

and as we made the southern seismic
shooting run on the Lord Howe
Rise we once again crossed
an outcrop of the basement.

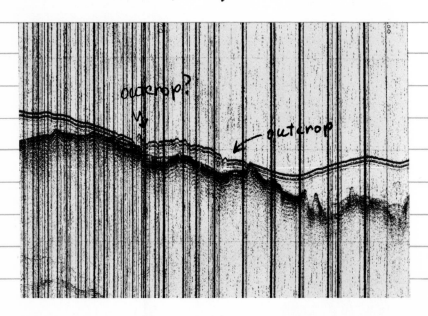

After the shooting was done we found the outcrop again and sampled it with a piston corer.

The sample slumped out of the core barrel and we tried to catch it in a bucket. Next we dredged and obtained basement rock, a fossil pelagic ooze about 15 million years old.

Illustrations from the
Challenger reports
show the delicate
structure of forams
living in surface
waters.

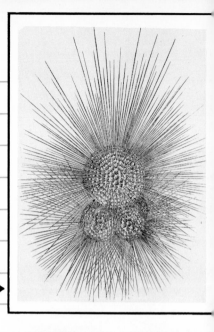

　　　Globigerina bulloides →
　　(greatly magnified)

When the forams die they
fall to the sea floor and
form a blanket of
pelagic ooze. The
delicate spines are
dissolved or broken off
by bottom currents shifting
the ooze.

The pelagic blanket may
be altered to solid lime-
stone or to phosphorite, as has
occurred here. The basement rocks
of the Lord Howe Rise are
similarly altered
foram ooze.

30

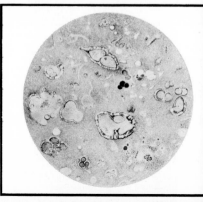

At last Leg V was over and we
turned south to the cooler latitude

Solomon
Summerhays
Francheteau
Karig
Menard

of Auckland. There some people
flew home and others joined the
expedition. The scientists went
to Wairaikei to see the
geological wonders and
boiling
lakes.

Francheteau

31

Karig        Francheteau

Then the ships separated and Horizon returned home through the tropics hotly pursued by sharks snapping at the magnetometer "fish."

**CHAPTER SEVEN** We celebrated the birth of the nation by sailing from Kings Wharf, Suva, in the late afternoon—once away from home there are no holidays even for modern oceanographers who expect to be home at Christmas. Several new members of the scientific party had never been to sea before, and we began instruction in how to stand a scientific watch. In general this involves learning how to use and not misuse a variety of instruments, how to communicate with the ship's officers on the bridge, and to sense difficulties in time to prevent them from developing. One must learn the speeds and operating conditions to pay out instruments behind the ship and haul them in. Most important, the watch stander has to keep accurate, detailed, legible records of what is happening: the depth, the intensity of the magnetic field, the water temperature, position of the ship, direction and speed of travel, wind speed and direction, and so on. Not all of these are necessary on every cruise, but they are typical of the diverse responsibilities of a scientific watch stander.

While two men stood the first watches, the others began housekeeping on the ship. At the beginning of a cruise or leg of a cruise life is relatively simple after all the instruments are working and before they have produced enough data for analysis. Consequently we made beds, spread out possessions in the tiny space available, and became acquainted with each

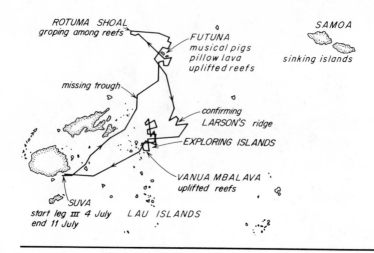

other and the ship. The weather leaving Suva was pleasant, and almost everyone was on deck to watch the island recede into the horizon. Soon we were through the pass in the reef and into the open sea. Even a slight swell causes a few people to want to lie down and avoid motion, so the groups on deck thinned. Moreover, we dine very early on our ships, and soon the heartier sailors were eating while their suffering shipmates wondered if they themselves would ever eat again.

As the night began to deepen we were surrounded by islands in all directions, hummocks of black velvet rising from the glossy black sea. To a sailor used to an unbroken horizon separating sea from sky, an island is mystically reassuring. The landsman sees an island as exotic, romantic, isolated, or whatever else it is that he is seeking at sea. The sailor a month or more at sea sees an island as an affirmation, irrefutable testimony that a world other than the ship still exists. Leaving Suva we were all as landsmen and could not but make wild surmises about the islands around us.

Meanwhile the southern skies opened above. One of the great delights of a small ship is that it is almost completely dark. When you come on deck only the great stars—Sirius, Procyon, Betelgeuse, Rigel—can be seen by light-sated eyes. In the total dark of the afterdeck more and more stars slowly appear as eyes adjust. In ten minutes, and minutes well spent, stars are everywhere. The Milky Way deserves its name, the Southern Cross shines brightly, and Venus is blinding. That night we saw several galaxies visible with the naked eye and verified them with binoculars. The sky was cloudless, the air warm, the sea calm, and the ship glided in beauty.

By the next day we were into the routine of discovery. The unsounded sea floor was being sounded every second as we sought a deep trough suggested by a few soundings in the area. We were working our way toward the island of Futuna and surveying targets of opportunity along the way. We cruised over hills and low mountains a mile and a half below and visible only on the echo sounder. However, after a while the distance between the bottom and the echo sounder is forgotten. As the marine geologist surveys a new range of undersea mountains, he senses them around him. I was once surveying with a captain new to the game. He remarked, as we headed again toward a peak on the map we were making, that he could not suppress a captain's feeling that we would hit it, even though he knew perfectly well it was a mile below the ship.

With an occasional convolution in the track to resolve some detail of the topography below, we continued on and arrived at Futuna at dawn. We put a boat over the side, loaded it with gear, and headed toward shore. Our purpose was to sample the island rocks and ultimately determine their age and history. We had very little information on the details of life on Futuna, in the sense of knowing whether we could expect to borrow or buy supplies or lodging. Consequently we had ready a mound of army cots, water in plastic containers, food from the ship's stock, and of course the scientific gear, such as sledge hammers, to collect the samples. Considering that the island was populated and under French administration it also seemed possible that a clean shirt and even a tie might prove necessary in case of an invitation to dinner by an island official. We were completely ignorant about our reception. We have landed on scores of islands, both announced and officially, and unannounced and unofficially, and have always been received very kindly. People on shore watch the ship approach the island and congregate at what they surmise is our landing site. Sometimes when a landing might be difficult a boat comes out to see if we want some help. When we set foot on shore the District Commissioner or an official with a similar title appears or we are taken to him. He asks who we are and if we have permission to land. Regardless of the answer he makes us welcome and when he understands that we want to collect some rock samples, and why, he usually loans us his Jeep or Land Rover and a driver to give us some help. We conclude a brief but productive stop by having a drink with the Commissioner and then collecting the mail to deliver to the next major port we reach. A thoroughly hospitable, efficient, and realistic operation. As the jet airfields and the bureaucrats multiply, however, life becomes more formal even in the remote Pacific. Consequently we had requested permission to land at Futuna through official channels but without any reply. Thus we were very pleased to be greeted by Le Resident de France, M. Philippe Aubin, who definitely was expecting us. After an exchange of pleasantries I explained that although everyone would like to stay ashore, most of the scientists, including myself, were obligated to keep the ship busy at sea and only a few could remain for two nights on Futuna. Within the hour *Horizon* was off again leaving Teddy Bullard, Jerry Winterer, three students, and the ship's physician marooned on what shortly turned out to be a very curious and interesting place.

Our goal at sea was to survey and dredge a shallow bank about sixty miles northwest of Futuna. We expected that, like other banks in the region, it would be covered with fossil limestone and thus we could do useful sampling to compare with that on land at Futuna. These banks have a remarkable characteristic: all that have been surveyed are only 60 to 100 feet deep but completely lack any shallower pinnacles. Thus they are readily accessible to sampling but do not menace the ship. Unfortunately, the bank we were approaching had not been surveyed. Moreover, the officers and crew were not used to such shallow banks and had difficulty believing that no rock would rise high enough to pierce the hull. Prudence and caution would quite rightfully be necessary. However, a ship is in no danger when the echo sounder shows water 1000 feet deep, and yet let an atmosphere of apprehension grow and the speed will be reduced on the grounds that it is prudent. Consequently when we were still in deep water and breakers were reported sighted nearby by a lookout, we turned toward them before faith was lost in the echo sounder. When the breakers proved a mirage, the tension eased out of the ship and we were ready to proceed, neither timidly nor foolhardily. Shortly thereafter we found our shoal and then could hardly make any further progress because it really was too shallow to risk rapid surveying. What we needed was a boat or two to sail ahead of us and sound for pinnacles. It was an eerie feeling to see bright coral sand between patches of dark coral rock clearly visible below the ship but concealed everywhere else around us by an unbroken sea. Moving very slowly we extricated ourselves from the bank without incident but then had some difficulty in finding the edge without again being trapped on the top. We repeatedly dredged limestone fragments suitable for dating. Ned Allison found nothing as old as the limestones on Futuna Island perhaps because they were here covered by recent reefs. We attempted to relocate a deep terrace on the side of the bank with the hope that it might be dredged of older material. However, by 2200 hours we had drifted so much that we could no longer establish our exact position relative to the shoal we had dredged, and we were in danger of wasting endless hours in futile groping on the top of the shallow bank. It seemed only sensible to start back toward Futuna while we still had enough time to do some useful surveying and more dredging. This we completed with the island visible to the southwest and by midafternoon we were ready to go ashore to learn what had happened. We were greeted by our dusty but enthusiastic comrades who showed us where they had slept in the tourist cottages which had just been finished at the water's edge—in case any tourists ever appeared. One cottage was just far enough out on the reef so it became an island at high tide, and a second was under construction. They should be very popular someday.

However, not yet, as M. Aubin shortly explained to us. The island is virtually inaccessible to tourists. Boats are infrequent and no airfield exists. When we inquired about mail, he made the curious remark that the mail went out once a month and was received twice a month. We were mystified until he explained that an airdrop of mail occurs monthly but no air pickup. Now roads and an airfield are planned and the island will have both frequent mail service and tourists.

As we drove along the only existing road we had a chance to see some of the attractions. The island, of course, is beautiful in the normal unspoiled Polynesian way. The sea sparkles, the reef foams, the coconut, papaya, mango, banana, and breadfruit grow, and the brown-skinned people smile. In short it has all the routine characteristics which would be so astonishing if they existed where most of us live. What then is unusual? Pigs. The pigs and other animals of Futuna are excluded from the interior by a continuous wall a few hundred feet in from the shoreline. The foundations of houses, coffer dams, and so on are all incorporated in this wall. We were told that it is more than ten miles long and was built about 200 years ago. Inside the wall, no animal lives and thus all the water that passes the wall is pure and drinkable. Between the wall and the sea live people, pigs, cattle, and chickens, all of which are sleek and healthy. The pigs roam about untended during the day but are individually owned. We were told each pig can recognize the tone of his household drum and comes running hoping to be fed when it beats. Certainly, at dusk, the pigs were sitting on their haunches like dogs, collected around people beating drums.

We were talking about hurricanes and how to survive by tying yourself to the bole of a topped coconut palm. The slight diameter of the palm offers little wind resistance and makes it admirable for the purpose. M. Aubin remarked on an unusual effect observed during the previous hurricane at Futuna when the wind speed was far above 100 miles per hour. The palms were unaffected, but as the wind increased the coconuts were pulled free and sailed through the air like cannonballs. We observed the dents in tin roofs which had somehow not been torn off.

The population is entirely Polynesian except for a very few Europeans. However, an occasional Melanesian custom has crossed over from the Fiji Islands. One is that some girls dress their hair in the spectacular Fijian style forming a great spherical halo. Another is that an occasional woman can be seen making a gesture of moving her finger across her throat as she looks at a passing visitor. This is a common gesture in the outlying Fijian Islands and we first thought it a most unfriendly indication that the gesturer would like to cut the visitor's throat. Nothing could be further from the truth. The gesture is said to mean "I shall cut my throat if you do not sleep with me."

The geology of the island also has Melanesian aspects. Two types of rock are common, basalt below and limestone above. The basalt is the dark rock poured out by the long-dead volcano which grew up first as an undersea mountain and finally as an island. The limestone is the remains of the reef and lagoon filling which collected around the volcanic island. Many millions of years ago Futuna looked like Bora Bora does now. The basalt in many places is of the type called "pillow lava" because it consists of a mass of spherical protrusions, or pillows, which form when a hot lava flow pushes forward into water by sending out sack-like buds about a yard in diameter. They never occur except under water. Thus many of the lavas of Futuna have been uplifted above sea level. Such pillow lavas are exceedingly rare in the great volcanic islands of the Pacific. In all the Hawaiian Islands, for example, only one doubtful occurrence exists. The central Pacific region, therefore, almost always sinks. In Fiji and New Caledonia and the continents, however, pillow lavas are observed, and thus these regions are sometimes elevated. Likewise the reefs of the central Pacific consistently sink on average and form atolls or deep banks. Our dredging of the previous night was on a drowned atoll produced by sinking. At Fiji, however, reef limestones in many places are uplifted, and they are as well in other places in Melanesia. Thus Futuna, which is in a position near the margin of the Fiji Plateau and of Melanesia, bears witness to a Melanesian rather than a Pacific type of vertical movement. Most of these events may have been initiated 10 million to 15 million years ago because the limestone is Miocene in age but uplift still continues. Within the last few years the sea floor at the mail landing at Sigave Bay has been elevated to such an extent that the quay is now too shallow for much use. The general level of the adjacent reef was elevated a foot or so above sea level, and most of the coral died.

The island of Vanua Mbalavu was our next destination for studies similar to those on Futuna. On our way we made some zigzags to test the existence of a long ridge suggested by one of the students, Roger Larson, on the basis of a few scattered sounding lines. He had the pleasure of proving that his speculation was correct and of verifying a great but unsuspected ridge more than 100 miles long. Shortly after dawn, at the time most favorable for approaching an unknown reef pass from the east, we entered the lagoon of the Exploring Islands. We had excellent charts prepared by the United States Exploring Expedition about 1840. The islands form a circle around a vast lagoon in the northern part of the Lau Islands, which lie half a day's run east of Fiji. Largest and westernmost of these Exploring Islands is Vanua Mbalavu with its harbor Loma Loma which sounds so similar to Point Loma at San Diego, where the Scripps fleet is based. The town of Loma Loma was once the port of entry for the Fiji area and was visited by several famous people who stayed in the hotels then available but now decayed. Again lacking knowledge of facilities, we loaded our boat with camping gear and headed for shore. This time Roger Larson was to have the experience of directing ship operations while the field party was ashore. This freed me to stay on the beach with Bullard, Winterer, and the others as the ship departed. No one seemed very interested in our arrival except a few children, although people strolling to Sunday church services nodded in passing. After a bit we located the chief official of the island, who was, moreover, the High Chief for the whole Lau group. With his Deputy, he happened to be on the island while the official yacht was being repaired. It soon developed that the Deputy High Chief urgently needed transportation to Suva to attend a reception for the Duke and Duchess of Kent, and was delighted to learn that we could shortly take him. Perhaps as a result of this but more likely because of exceptional standards of hospitality we soon found ourselves residents in the home of a deceased High

Chief. It was quickly opened, prepared, carpeted with mats, garnished with furniture, and we were properly based for our work.

We began by employing a sizable native launch with outboard motor, boatman, and two native guides. We then divided into two parties, paleomagnetic and paleontological, each in its own boat, and headed off to sample. These arrangements proved to be most judicious. The rock samples we collect tend to be large, and hauling them by boat was very efficient. Moreover, our native guides were invaluable in finding ways through the reef passes to the beach and through the jungle to outcrops. I insert these rather apologetic words because of the general American attitude, which was certainly our attitude, that it is downright imperialistic to have a native bearer. However, the residents of a place are called "natives" and they turn out to be better informed about the place than visitors (whatever called). It was a lot of fun cruising along in small boats, discussing the geology, picnicking on the beach, smashing off the oriented samples, and finally returning to the residence. Teddy, Jerry, and I decided to walk across the narrow but steep island rather than boat back with the samples. We hoped to do some collecting in the higher hills. Guided along, we marched through the jungle and then into Loma Loma from the interior. The village was beautifully kept, resembling Suva in the clean, neat grass, and orderly flowering bushes. Our temporary home was on a vast grassy square surrounded by large houses. We chatted until dark, improvised a dinner including hot frankfurters and coffee as well as more picnic supplies, and fabricated our cots. We remarked to one of our hosts about the cleanliness of the village and inquired about the water supply (we were drinking ship water out of plastic containers as usual). He said all the island water was drinkable, and the village clean for one reason only, namely all the pigs were confined to small pens. A curious contrast to Futuna, but leading to the same result. I am reminded of the fact that it is illegal to put packages overhead in American airplanes because they might fall on the passengers, so we put them on the floor. It is illegal to put packages on the floor in Russian airplanes because they might prevent passengers from moving to the exits, so they put them overhead. Pigs or passengers, all are herded about by bureaucrats.

We were up at dawn for more sampling. Wandering about to get a match to light the fire I discovered why the grass was so neat. A girl was sweeping it with a long broom —at 5 in the morning. We sampled here and sampled there and returned to the village to meet the ship in the afternoon. As our boat approached shore we noticed one woman fishing on the reef who made a friendly gesture of cutting her throat with her finger when we waved. The geology was equally Melanesian, consisting of interlayered limestone and lava flows all of which were of the same age and had been uplifted like those at Futuna. With this new evidence that the sea floor of the Fiji Plateau had been elevated, we boarded *Horizon*, which had finished surveying and then been delayed when she almost ran aground on an uncharted reef at the entrance to the American Passage. Soon we were under way for Suva, but the delay made visibility poor at the nearby exit from the reef, and we had to pass the length of the lagoon to again reach the deep sea.

We were off Suva by noon, saw *Argo*, and went through a baffling exercise of bringing the two ships alongside each other out in the harbor in order to exchange explosives. Harmon Craig, chief scientist on *Argo*, and I each thought the other had laid on this exercise and wondered why. Soon it developed that it was a creation of our ship's agent in Suva who had been so directed by George Shor some months before according to the plans for exchanging explosives then current. Finally we got both ships to the dock.

# Leg IV The High and Hot Plateau

**CHAPTER EIGHT** We spent 11 to 13 July at Suva again, in part for rest and recreation but mainly for engine repairs. We also grossly revised our plans on the basis of a new chart issued by the British Admiralty in April 1967 after *Argo* and *Horizon* left San Diego. It showed a safe passage from Bligh Waters north of Viti Levu Island through the great reef to the open waters on the north. All previous charts indicated that the reef was impassible except by small boat—which was how Captain Bligh crossed in the longboat from the *Bounty*. This new chart would permit us to follow in Bligh's track, shorten our travel toward Rotuma, eliminate duplication of a lot of our older soundings, and allow us to make measurements with a ship in the shallow waters between the large continental type of Fiji Islands. We were offered the same kind of opportunity to explore a continent with our shipborne geophysical tools that we would have passing through the Suez Canal or up the Mississippi—an exciting prospect.

Most of the *Horizon* crew spent the evening of the 12th watching a movie on the ship, and thus it did not appear that any strong pressure existed to stay at Suva. We sailed on the morning of the 13th and turned east into the swell again to round Viti Levu. About sunset we entered Bligh Waters. To the south was the coastline of Viti Levu, which Bligh discovered and surveyed in his fantastic voyage in an open boat. To the

**113**

north was the great dark outline of Vanua Levu, and all about were the myriad of small islands from which cannibal-laden canoes came out to pursue the harrassed but loyal crew from the *Bounty*. It was a great saga to visualize on the spot. Some of us had the pleasure of watching a green flash as the sun disappeared into Bligh Waters. These "flashes" are a delicate green light which appears just after the sun sets. This was a very good flash because the ship dropped into a trough, the sun appeared to set, and then the ship rose on a swell just in time to make the green flash visible. Most of the students on deck had never seen one and did not see this flash and expressed the common skepticism that it exists. Fortunately it was photographed in color by the Vatican Observatory in Italy some years ago, and the matter should no longer be in dispute.

We knew from the British survey that the bottom of Bligh Waters would be smooth and probably uninteresting, so our hope was that we would discover some unusual magnetic anomalies which might reflect the deep rock structure under a smooth cover of mud and sand. We quickly found several quite intense anomalies and surveyed one which was roughly circular. This was a disappointment because if it had been linear we might have been able to relate it to the geology of the surrounding islands. Circular anomalies would require much more time to investigate than we had available, and we had to press on.

By morning we emerged from Bligh Waters into the open sea, which was not as calm as one might like. As will develop, I am writing this section on *Argo* during the second week in August after we left Noumea because for the next several weeks on *Horizon* it was calm enough to use a typewriter for only a few hours. Of course I wrote notes about events and our developing thoughts, and the expedition scientific logs contain an average of one notation each minute for all the months that the ships are at sea. Moreover, the scientific instruments record several things each second, so the past is not beyond recall in oceanography. Our problems with the sea were to be far more important than the absence of good typing conditions and ultimately would reduce us to almost complete impotence as an expedition. All this was in the future. On the

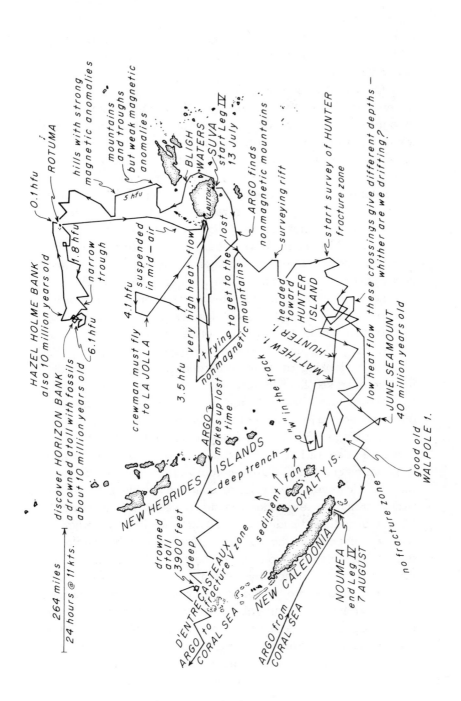

264 miles
24 hours @ 11 kts.

HAZEL HOLME BANK
also 10 million years old

discover HORIZON BANK
a drowned atoll with fossils
about 10 million years old

0.1 hfu
ROTUMA

hills with strong
magnetic anomalies

mountains
and troughs
but weak magnetic
anomalies

1.8 hfu
narrow
trough

6.1 hfu

5 hfu

BLIGH
WATERS

SUVA
start Leg IV
13 July

ARGO finds
nonmagnetic mountains

surveying rift

start survey of HUNTER
fracture zone

crewman must fly
to LA JOLLA

4.1 hfu
suspended
in mid-air

very high heat flow

3.5 hfu
nonmagnetic mountains

trying to get to the
lost

ARGO
makes up lost
time

headed
toward
HUNTER
ISLAND

MATTHEW I.
HUNTER I.

low heat flow these crossings give different depths —
whither are we drifting?

NEW HEBRIDES ISLANDS

deep trench

"in the track"

JUNE SEAMOUNT
40 million years old

good old
WALPOLE 1.

drowned
atoll
3900 feet
deep

D'ENTRECASTEAUX
fracture zone
ARGO to
CORAL SEA

sediment fan

LOYALTY IS.

NEW CALEDONIA

NOUMEA
end Leg IV
7 AUGUST

ARGO from
CORAL SEA

no fracture zone

morning of Bastille Day we merely pitched and tossed a bit and a few people were seasick as we began the work that was taking us north.

Our objectives on Leg IV were diverse but related to the general problems of the expedition. We wanted to survey the topography and magnetic anomalies of a belt of faulted and fractured submarine mountains north and west of Viti Levu. These mountains were the locus of earthquakes and might be similar to the center of sea floor spreading at the crest of the Mid-Atlantic Ridge. If so they would give crucial information about the development of the region. Second, we wanted to see if we could correlate anything with the great shallow region of the Fiji Plateau. Why was it shallow? We were looking for clues, and within our capabilities, the measurement of heat flow appeared most promising. When was it formed? The best information would come from dredging ancient rocks from the sea floor and chipping them from islands. The samples by their composition would tell us much of the history of the region if we could date them. Finally, we hoped to study the Fiji Plateau by looking at its margins and seeing how it graded into the deep sea floor to north and south. The edge of a geological structure—like the edge of the new type of American quarter—may reveal much of what is concealed in the middle.

We began with the two-mile-deep trough just north of the Great Sea Reef of Fiji. It proved to be a long thin feature such as might be created by the numerous earthquakes which occur along it. However, it was not as continuously deep as we expected from the few older crossings. Perhaps it is partially filled with sediment sliding and rolling down from the adjacent reef. We noticed in the course of the topographic survey a quite unexpected relationship, namely, the submarine topography was not matched by related magnetic anomalies. Undersea mountains are almost always volcanoes formed of rock containing iron-rich minerals which affect a magnetometer. Depending on the state of the earth's field when the lavas cooled, the rock produces either a large positive or large negative anomaly. Likewise the linear troughs and ridges of the midocean mountains have a very large central magnetic anomaly. Thus the undersea mountains we were surveying were quite exceptional. We did not yet know whether we were observing a characteristic of the region or just of this one spot, but in any event it would bear watching. Two developments quickly followed that highlighted the relationship between topography and magnetics as a promising subject for further work. First we found as we sailed north that the sea floor changed from mountainous to hilly; if exposed it would look like the Poconos, whereas just north of Fiji it would resemble the Colorado Rockies. Oddly enough, the magnetic anomalies were much too large both in quantity and size to be produced by the hills and clearly were the result of something else. The second development was that we talked with Jerry Winterer on *Argo*, which had also crossed the large submarine mountains near Fiji, but on the southwest side rather than on the north like *Horizon*. He had also observed that the mountains were nonmagnetic and that magnetic anomalies occurred over the hilly plateau further from Fiji. We were already on to some significant regional relationship, but further investigation would have to wait until next we came to Fiji from Rotuma.

The heat flow problem developed in just the right sequence to provide a maximum of excitement for a few weeks. It provided all the necessary elements of a good mystery: a wild surmise, early confirmation, secondary doubts, a complication in the plot, increasing certainty, increasing conflict with a powerful opponent (namely weather), and a satisfactory solution. Agatha Christie could have outlined the whole story, but it was fun living it. The surmise that we discussed as we sailed north was that the Fiji Plateau might have high heat flow. This was based on the fact that four of seven pre-*Nova* measurements in this region were higher than the normal and extremely widespread value of 1.2 heat flow units (microcalories per square centimeter per second). However, three values were normal or below and, anyway, seven values in an area of half a million square miles, even though a uniformly shallow area, provide little basis for a surmise. A comparable conjecture would be to parachute through the clouds to an unknown land, wander through the fog, hear girlish voices, meet seven girls, observe that four are blondes, notice a geographical fact, namely that it is cold, and then surmise that you are in Sweden and that almost all the unseen girls are very blond. The probability of the two surmises being correct was, at that time, about the same. That is, considering the populations in the various races of man, the chance of parachuting into a place where most of the girls are very blond is extremely remote. Although heat flow measurements are far less abundant than girls and thus the statistics are by no means as good, nevertheless only one region of uniformly high heat flow had been found on earth, and it under the Sea of Japan. A prediction that the Fiji Plateau was another such region thus was strongly against the odds.

Nevertheless the first measurement made during *Nova* near Fiji was 3.5 heat flow units or almost three times normal. As we sailed north we awaited the next measurement with varying thoughts. Teddy Bullard, who made some of the first successful measurements sixteen years before, was soon to witness about the 1200th. John Sclater, in charge of the measurements, was wondering if everything would work in a complex sequence of necessary events. Big George Hohnhaus, who was in charge of all sampling operations, was concerned with the deteriorating weather. I was wondering how much ship time we should allot to heat flow during the next few days, considering the other possibilities. I think, however, that we all felt about the same emotion—the thrill of the hunt. Our excitement mounted as the probe came aboard, the case was opened, the record removed, recording paper extracted, and then Sclater reported a measurement of about 5 heat flow units or one of the highest measurements ever made.

Soon I was radioing our results to Winterer on *Argo* and he reported a measurement far west of ours but still well within the Fiji Plateau. He had found a value of 4.1 units or well over three times normal. Now we were really elated.

Our speculations regarding bottom topography were based on more facts than those on heat flow but were not coming out so well. We were confronted with a scale problem. The very large topographic features were already known. We had hoped that we could discover and map somewhat smaller features such as fault troughs a few hundred miles long which would help to unravel the history of the region. What we were finding was that the topography was extremely complex with large numbers of mountains which were too small to map without accurate positioning and a large amount of time. In short we had no chance of seeing the forest because of the trees. We decided to concentrate on a few small surveys and skip the planned program. At least we might hope to find the trend of a few fault scarps or volcanoes and these trends might show how the crust was deformed.

Early on 16 July we marooned another of Teddy Bullard's field groups on Rotuma Island to obtain oriented rock samples for paleomagnetism and recent shells and fossils for paleontology. Included were two students who had been seasick since leaving Suva and had been unable to stand watches. It seemed only a mercy to put them on solid ground for a few days. Ned Allison and I went ashore only to see that suitable accommodations were available before getting *Horizon* under way again for more oceanography.

First we went into deep water southwest of Rotuma and made a heat flow station. It was successful, but the value was only 1.8 units or barely 1½ times normal. We were approaching the northern edge of the plateau; were we also approaching the edge of the high heat flow region? Did such a region really exist? We surveyed and dredged two seamounts and then a trough in line with one of them; then we measured another heat flow—1.5 units. Next we approached a shallow undersea mountain indicated by one of the many sounding lines we had acquired from other organizations. The bottom kept going up and up and up as we changed scale on the depth recorder until it leveled at 70 feet, deepened slightly and then rose again to 70 feet before dropping abruptly into water two miles deep. What we had just discovered was a drowned atoll—an addition to the dozens already known in this region. These features have the same shape, size and composition as atolls except that they are slightly submerged. Why they exist is a mystery. Certainly they were exposed above sea level when it was much lower a few thousand years ago. Why did they not grow upward like other atolls as sea level rose? Perhaps new dredging would tell. There is always a bonus in discovering a mountain—you get to name it. The names applied to deep submarine mountains appear only on specialized scientific charts, but a "bank," defined as a mountain with a top less than 600 feet deep, goes on all navigation charts and thus achieves a far broader measure of fame. This was a new bank but what should we call it? Considering everything it seemed appropriate to name it after the ship, "Horizon Bank," following a common custom. The old ship already had given a name to various features discovered aboard her, but banks are hard to find these days and we thought that she deserved one last tribute.

We dredged Horizon Bank at two levels and Ned Allison began to see a pattern. On several seamounts we obtained fossils of Pliocene or possibly Miocene age which showed that submarine volcanoes had existed several million years ago and perhaps as much as 10 million years. This was far younger than the nearby drowned atoll we had dredged on the *Capricorn* Expedition some years before. However, that atoll had been one of a different and distinct line and possibly the line of volcanoes we were studying was younger.

From Horizon Bank we went into deep water and determined the heat flow as a spectacularly high 6.1 units. Our luck on *Horizon* was holding but the heat flow program on the Fiji Plateau planned for *Argo* had collapsed after one more attempted measurement. Because of an unexpected stop at Lautoka and heavy weather, Winterer had had to abandon the integrated plan for a line of seismic stations and accompanying sampling and heat flow from Fiji across the plateau to the New Hebrides. Somehow we would have to make up this work with *Horizon* or abandon our hopes for any understanding of the Fiji Plateau.

We continued surveying around Horizon Bank and measured a heat flow to the northwest. The value was an extremely low 0.1 or less than 10 percent of normal. What could this mean? Was the measurement erroneous or misleading because of one of the numerous events or circumstances that can affect the apparent value of heat flow? Was it real and significant in the sense that we were very near the margin of the plateau and also the possible region of high heat flow? The topography at the edges of the plateau includes many great deep troughs. Did the heat flow also go through some minimum value in grading from high to normal in the deep Pacific to the north? Sclater, as the man most closely involved, was most skeptical about the significance of the low value.

We went east to dredge Hazel Holme Bank, which is another drowned atoll. Once again Ned Allison quickly identified Pliocene and probably Miocene fossils as well as living corals. The dredge hauls from these banks contained an unusual variety of fragments of volcanic rock, fragments of reef limestone, lithified ooze composed of microscopic calcareous shells, and glassy black crusts of *pahoehoe*, the very fluid type of lava with a ropey surface like fudge, just like the flows now seen emerging from Hawaiian volcanoes.

Eastward we continued to meet our arrival time to pick up the people at Rotuma. They were staying five days on the island, which was more than we estimated would be necessary for the land work but was about right to complete the planned work at sea. We hoped that they were not bored but it seemed most improbable on a friendly island where wine is commonly made from wild oranges. On we went, taking a heat flow value of 4 units, then another of 1.8, then some surveying, then a heat flow of 0.1 northeast of Rotuma, followed by a repeated measurement at the same site to test the accuracy of the measurement, also 0.1 units. Clearly low heat flow occurred in several places associated with the northern margin of the Fiji Plateau.

We retrieved the Rotuma field party at dawn and headed south toward Lautoka in western Viti Levu, the port nearest Nadi International Airport. On the way we planned to survey the trend of some supposed linear troughs and measure more heat flow. Just south of Rotuma we discovered a large submarine volcano with the same area and trend but less height than Rotuma. The weather had remained steadily bad but not to the point of affecting operations, and with all the people prone to seasickness on shore we had more or less ignored it. Now it definitely worsened again. The ship headed directly into the swell in great pitching surges. The expected ridges and troughs were only partially confirmed and certainly are very complex. Still our topographic-magnetic relationship

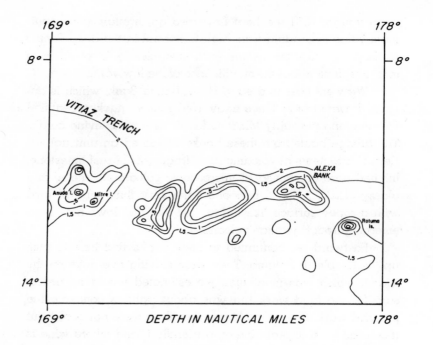

DEPTH IN NAUTICAL MILES

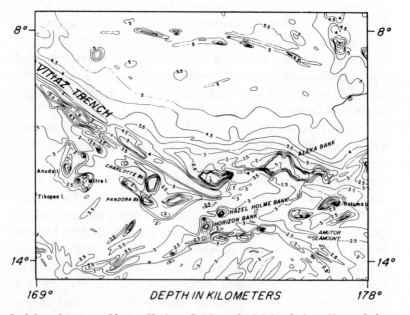

DEPTH IN KILOMETERS

Redoing the map. Above, Horizon Bank and vicinity before *Nova*; below, after *Nova*.

seemed to hold: complex topography–smooth magnetics, smoother but hilly topography–large-scale magnetic anomalies. We got another confirming relationship from heat flow with one more spectacular value of 5 units.

There was little discussion of the new results because of general fatigue from the weather and lack of sleep. We discovered in discussions the next morning that at least two lurches of the ship that last night woke everyone who was momentarily asleep. The ship surged upward at the peak of a swell and fell into the trough. We all awoke suspended in mid-air. The memory of such events is persistent. Just after dawn we passed through the reef entrance, picked up a pilot and went through smooth waters to Lautoka. There a few scientists departed as scheduled. With them went the two students who never had recovered from seasickness and were unable to work while sick. They were miserable and obviously had no future as deep sea oceanographers so it was time for them to go home and work at something else. We sailed west to fill in the gap in data left by *Argo*. The weather was still wretched but again we observed that the submarine mountains near Fiji were nonmagnetic. We still had no clue why. We measured heat flow at about sixty-mile intervals: 3.6, 5.0, 1.8, 2.6— what a series! Then came a value of 0.3 units. Were we nearing the edge of the region of high heat flow? If so it did not correspond exactly with the shallow Fiji Plateau which continued on to the New Hebrides Islands. The next value west was 3.5 and the next to the southeast was 3.2. The low value was thus an anomaly and it remains unexplained.

Our intention was to sail west almost to the New Hebrides Islands and thus make a complete profile across the plateau. This would complement an earlier and less complete profile to the south which was made by our *Proa* Expedition several years earlier. Then we were going to survey the southern edge of the Fiji Plateau. About this time, however, a possible explanation for the topographic-magnetic relationship near Fiji came up for discussion during bull sessions on *Horizon*. It went as follows: (1) rivers and waves transport sand and mud to the ocean bordering continents and large islands; (2) this sediment generally collects as a thick wedge which forms a smooth transition between the high continents and the deep ocean floor; (3) Fiji ought to be surrounded by such a smooth wedge of sediment; (4) instead it is circled by nonmagnetic mountains which are still forming if we could judge by numerous earthquakes; (5) therefore perhaps the wedge of sediment had existed and had been broken by faulting and formed into mountains which are nonmagnetic because they are made of nonmagnetic sedimentary rocks such as limey mud. Put in this form the idea sounds formal or even legalistic but of course it evolved gradually. In science in general and geology in particular, ideas are what money is to bankers, an absolute necessity. The equivalents of many economic laws apply. For example, those who have some get more and more, and those with few get less and less. Practice at thinking works like compound interest. Science grows exponentially because of the inverse of Gresham's law, namely the good ideas or hypotheses drive out the bad. The basic problem in geology and geophysics is to identify the good ones. This is impossible unless someone can think of a test or verify a prediction. Any hypothesis worth discussing can explain the facts known at the time. A good hypothesis forms the basis for a prediction which can be tested. If it cannot be tested it is not much help.

How could we test the nonmagnetic mountain hypothesis? In these days of advancing technology we tend to solve problems with new tools and thus sub-bottom profiling seemed attractive. It is not difficult to forecast the internal structure that would be expected if a sedimentary wedge became faulted into mountains. With this thought in mind, we continued to follow our plan of measuring heat flow. Suddenly, perhaps "at last" is more appropriate, the idea of dredging the nonmagnetic mountains was proposed. A wedge of sediment is not unlike a beginning cook's layer cake which rises on only one side. If you cut such a cake all the layers are exposed. If our hypothesis was correct, faulting had cut the sedimentary wedge and the layers were exposed on the faulted mountain sides. There is nothing more maddening than thinking of a plausible hypothesis, conceiving a test, and then being unable to conduct it. We wanted to dredge as soon as possible. This required a change in plans but after all the plans were completely flexible and meant to be changed in just this way.

We had to sail east—back toward Fiji, which was a little annoying after having been there several times. It was also not to be as easy as sailing west from Fiji because the wind and swell were from the east. Once again we began to beat into the weather and once again it seemed to get worse, as though it were saving up its energy to attack when we were most helpless. We sailed unsteadily east, splitting the distance between our other track lines in the region so as to get the maximum amount of information. Among other things this line helped to define the topography and the shape of the magnetic anomalies in the central region of the plateau. However, as the weather deteriorated the drift of the ship increased and the position became more uncertain. Early on the 26th the sky was clear enough to obtain a star fix by moonlight. Between then and dawn we apparently drifted ten miles south. Between dawn and dusk we drifted fourteen miles west of our calculated position by dead reckoning. As night set in the seas were up to twenty feet high and the wind was above 30 knots. We have worked on *Horizon* in somewhat worse weather, especially in higher winds, but the most difficult thing to do in bad weather is dredge in deep water and that was our objective. We continued east trying to find a particular trough identified on earlier legs of the expedition. We were navigating by the bottom topography just as it is done on land, except by land standards we had such a bad map that we had to remake it as we went along. At one point it seemed that we had reached our destination, although we were bouncing about so much and the bottom was so steep and the waves were making our records so noisy that we could hardly even measure the depth. At that time we thought that if we could find just the right spot where we could dredge *up* a cliff and *toward* the weather we might just manage it. Then we slowed the ship to retrieve the magnetometer and its long cable; as we picked up speed and turned toward the proposed dredging site the echo sounder stopped recording. Fifteen minutes later it was operating but when we turned the ship toward the dredging site, the cliff was gone. Where was it? Where were we? How could we relocate it without a lengthy survey which we could not make without better soundings than we could get in such weather? Could we still dredge when we did find the cliff? We decided that the potential gain did not equal the certain cost, and that we should do something that we could do. That was not much, but if we sailed southwest we would be going with the weather, would not pitch so much, and could at least get decent soundings and a magnetic record. Upwind we could do nothing. Downwind we went.

By morning we had a position again and everyone was somewhat rested after a little sleep. We continued to survey with about the same waves around us but less wind. We were encouraged to attempt another heat flow measurement which is neither as difficult nor as lengthy as dredging. Even so, the operations of lowering the instruments over the side, holding the ship in position, and recovering the instruments were barely safe for people and not without hazard for about $15,000 worth of instruments on the end of 1½ miles of thin wire. The measurement was only partially successful and indicated a much higher value than normal. It seemed unduly risky to attempt to verify the measurement; we continued south toward the southern edge of the Fiji Plateau, which is called the Hunter fracture zone.

This zone contained some active volcanic islands, and numerous sounding lines showed several very deep troughs and some submarine volcanoes. The relief was very similar to the northern boundary of the Fiji Plateau except that the deeps were deeper and there were no drowned atolls. The two boundaries were likewise similar in that they lacked earthquakes in most places, although the Hunter fracture zone was active at its western end. There an interesting problem existed regarding the nature of the intersection between the fracture zone trending northeast and the New Hebrides Trench, a great deep, trending north-northwest. Did one change into the other or one cut off the other? If the latter, the one cut off would be the older, if the former they probably were contemporaneous and had the same origin. In addition to surveying topography we also wanted to measure more heat flow and particularly to dredge with the hope springing eternal that at the edge of the plateau we could cut into the lower crustal layers.

Over the edge of the plateau and across the great roller coaster of the fracture zone we went in a sea of ringing echoes as the pings from the sounder ricocheted off the steep walls below. The weather fought us all the way. We did not see the morning stars, we did not see the sun at noon, we did not see the evening stars, we did not see the moon. After two days without celestial positions we began to feel a little too lost. We had crossed from the plateau at 1600 fathoms to a narrow trough at 3272 fathoms and into the northern edge of the South Fiji Basin at 2400 fathoms. We had recrossed the trough. We had crossed undersea volcanoes and fault blocks. And from time to time we had checked our surveying by recrossing our own sounding lines to see whether we got the same depth. We did not. Clearly we were drifting under the influence of the wind and swell, but in what direction? The swell came from one direction and the wind from another. We had to go at very slow speeds if we turned toward the east or else the pitching ship put air under the echo sounder and we could not measure the depth. If we went very slowly, the drift, which presumably was constant, became quantitatively more important. If we tried to sail southeast, the drift might cause us to move directly south, but who could tell? Somehow we had to find ourselves. Less than 100 miles or eight hours running to the west was Hunter Island and even farther west was Matthew. Both are tiny active volcanoes, uninhabited by man, beast, or even many plants. However they are several hundred feet high and thus make good radar reflectors, which is just what we needed. We could detect either twenty-five miles away and we could not possibly be so lost that we could not find such big targets. We still had ample time in reserve to improvise useful work, and the weather 100 miles away might be good enough so that we could do some sampling. I asked the officer on watch on the bridge to head toward where he thought Hunter Island might be and change direction to pass near it once he had detected it on radar.

Several hours later we picked up the island and sailed

nearby well before dawn. The moon was shining brightly on the sterile dark shape and shadows danced on the water. Matthew Island we passed after dawn. A black cone of cinders with a few optimistic patches of green which had taken root since the last eruption. Now firmly located, we headed north onto the southern edge of the Fiji Plateau. After sailing about thirty miles to get away from the influence of the volcano, we took a heat flow measurement which was normal as blueberry pie, 1.1 units. But was it only normal because it was on a steep gradient between the high values of the plateau and other lower values in the fracture zone? Or did the boundary of the high heat flow and of the plateau not coincide here? We needed more measurements and they would have to be to the east but that was into the weather and would be a complete waste of time. We could not take soundings heading into the swell, and we could barely recover the heat probe where we were. It would be impossible in worse weather to the east. We still had adequate time to improvise and decided to make a great loop to the west to survey the junction of the fracture zone and the New Hebrides Trench. That would allow a few days for the weather to abate and then we could work again toward the east and fill in our planned dredging and heat flow stations. We could also complete our survey of the fracture zone now that we knew where we were and thus could calculate where we had been.

Calculations of ocean drift are still made in about the same way that Maury did in the nineteenth century in order to provide information for American clipper ships. A ship determines its position by seeing a known island or more often by sightings on the moon, sun, planets, and stars. It then sets a compass course and sails along until it can again determine a position, usually at sunset or sunrise because it is necessary during a star fix to see both the stars, i.e. dark, and the horizon, i.e. light. Having a new position, the ship commonly finds it is not where it should be if it sailed in the direction indicated by its compass and at the speed indicated by its log. The difference is its drift. Thus it is quite possible to make a survey of the sea floor which is puzzling at the time but can be all straightened out once the position of the ship is again known.

When we detected Hunter Island on our radar we started to calculate the track backward to our previous fix and shortly had established where we had been in the Hunter fracture zone in a manner that made the depths agree where our track crossed over itself. The newly mapped topography, nonetheless, seemed a fantastic jumble and we wanted more soundings to see just what was there.

Scripps had already surveyed part of the southern New Hebrides Trench and our friends from the Institute of Oceanology in Moscow had made a trench crossing further south. We decided to make our first crossing about twenty miles further south still and then work toward the south and east making repeated crossings of the deep until it did or did not join the Hunter fracture zone. I left word to wake me at midnight or when the water deepened as we again went off the edge of the plateau—whichever came first. I had a few glorious hours of sleep as we ran downwind to the west but found my will was beginning to weaken when I was awakened at midnight. "Wake me again at 2000 fathoms." I said. An hour later I woke with a start. What had happened? Why were we not in the trench? Surely we were not lost again already? Surely all the previous sounding in the region was not wrong? I went over the sounding log and other records with the scientific watch stander. All was well, we had no reason to believe that we were lost and the sounder was performing adequately. It appeared that the long trench did not continue this far south or else was greatly constricted. I went back to sleep, leaving instructions to turn south in a few hours. At 0500 hours the echo sounder suddenly started recording noise and the bottom was hardly visible on the records. We were headed south parallel to the swell and the noise was not connected with the weather or any change in course or speed. Something was wrong in the electronics of the machine or the electrical power. We reduced speed to a minimum and the electronics technician and the electrician began to seek a solution. The latest model echosounder recorder has the electronic circuitry broken into easily replaceable parts. Thus a complete overhaul takes little time. When finished, the record was improved but still not very useful. We were recording only a little more than electrical noise from the ship. By the usual field repair technique of fiddling with all controls and wires it was found that one of the ship's alternating current circuits had noise and the other did not. That problem was solved. One of the control knobs on the back of the recorder was in the wrong position and apparently had been struck by something or someone when the ship and its contents intersected on a roll. That was adjusted and we had a good record again. However we were in water only a mile and a half deep and on a favorable course. What could we record in deep water when moving into the weather? We changed course to recross the trench and quickly found out— nothing.

We had reached the end of the line. We were at the westernmost part of the area of interest and could not go further downwind. We could not dredge, core, or measure heat flow. At any reasonable speed we could not measure the depth to the east and that was where we wanted to go. We could measure the magnetic field but it would be meaningless without the depth. The only thing left of our potent scientific armory was the absolute minimum—we could still maneuver. And so we turned into the weather, not to collect records but, like a bark of yore, to tack upwind to where we could again turn and work downweather. I could not remember being reduced to these straits before but as we bounced along from swell to swell I was amused at the thought of our track once this maneuver was finished. The track of a ship usually goes rather smoothly in some general direction and the final plot of a survey looks about like a longhand writing exercise of a line of "e's" or "l's." This time we would be making something more like a "w" because we would reverse our course in the middle. We could continue to maneuver the ship so the plotted soundings would spell out initials or make a simple picture. I have sometimes tried to visualize the assigned goals of modern science if a Roman emperor, for example, were suddenly in charge. Would science and technology be used to blow each other to bits or to increase the speed of jet planes? I doubt it very much. Nero, I surmise, would use them for entertainment. It has been argued that the space programs of the United States and Russia are now intended as entertainment but I mean something more personal. Visualize a complicated series of launchings of satellites along different orbits, the expenditure of a few billion dollars in rocket fuel. After some weeks of this the emperor would lead his birthday guests onto the terrace in the cool of evening. Flashing from all directions would come the satellites and at precisely the anniversary of his birth the sky would spell "Nero."

Since the expedition was not financed as marine sport, we continued to take a beating going into the sea for several hours and then turned back to sound. We were getting records at last. We crossed the trench south of our previous track and found that it was deep. Our first crossing had merely been at a constriction in a still continuing trench. Soon we were west again and the weather had not abated and the water east was presumably still deep. Did we have to write another "w" on our track? By turning so the swell came at an angle to the bow, and slowing to about one-half speed we found we could collect usable results and plunged again toward the deep. I never saw a man who looked with such a wistful eye as a navigator after a day without sighting the sky. It was getting to be a long time between star fixes again. We had not crossed our own sounding track but we had crossed many older ones. Either they were all wrong since our electrical troubles or else we were drifting rapidly toward the west. Well before dawn the next morning we were nervousing about the amount of this drift. The published charts showed that with enough drift we would be onto L'Orne Rock although usually this would not give too much of a problem because our echo sounders would show when the water was becoming dangerously shallow. However, the *Sailing Directions* indicated that the water just next to the rock was deep and thus we might ground on the rock before we could stop unless we went very slowly for a long time. We were suffering from something I had only read about—we needed a fix. A cloudy dawn, of doubtful navigational value, was some hours away but there on the map (to the southwest?) was a small island with vertical walls 300 feet high, in short the very model of a radar target. We calculated we could detect it at twenty-five miles and then estimated the best course to spot it without

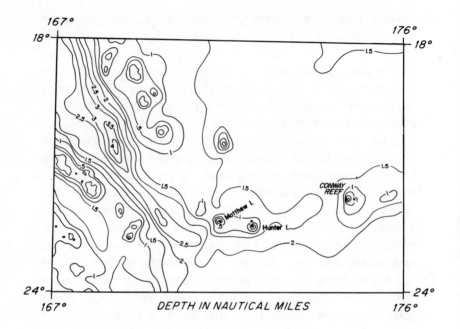

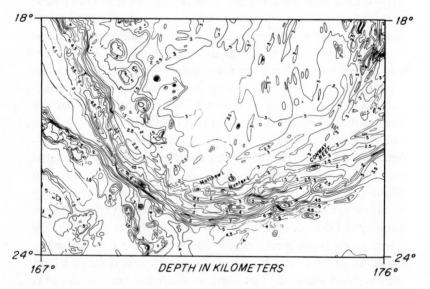

**Redoing the map. Above, the Hunter fracture zone before** *Nova;* **below, after** *Nova.*

increasing the hazard from L'Orne Rock. Walpole Island, the *Sailing Directions* speak harshly of your ironbound coast and infertile center but we loved you when you came in on the radar a few minutes after our turn. We had drifted twenty miles off course but quickly worked out about where we had been and found that our soundings agreed better with the older ones. Some puzzling discrepancies remained as we turned southeast for another crossing of the trench.

At last the weather began to moderate. We picked up speed and still got usable records on the sounder. The sky cleared by dawn and a star fix was followed through the morning by the less accurate but very useful positions determined by sightings on the sun. The star fix showed that we had drifted west since our radar fix on Walpole Island. However, even correcting for a westward drift we did not seem to be able to intersect the trench. After some time we turned northeast to see if the trench had ended or whatever. The bottom quickly deepened as we went into the axis of the trench but somehow the axis did not line up with the previous crossings and trenches are generally without sharp kinks. Our noon position seemed to be of good quality but made no sense at all when compared to our dead reckoning course. Having crossed the trench we turned south. The successive sun lines indicated we were being set to the west but on closer inspection it developed that the ship had to have a following current to give it the observed speed, and that would require a drift to the south. Something was very wrong and had been for some time. We realized that sometimes we appeared to drift east and sometimes west and sometimes south but no matter what our course we always drifted to the right. That has been impossible since the Greek gods stopped directing the winds for their own purposes. The only way to go consistently to the right is to have an error in the steering system and such we had. The gyroscopic repeater in the automatic pilot was steering 4° to the right. Since when? No one will ever know, but it appeared that it might have been at the time we had electrical troubles and developed electrical noise in our echo sounder. Until then the navigation and soundings made sense, afterwards they did not.

Our minds were much more at ease after the cause of our navigation troubles was uncovered. We crossed the trench for the sixth time and after replotting the soundings found that it turned in a smooth curve from north-northwest to east. The New Hebrides Trench graded into the Hunter fracture zone without a sign of any truncated structures. The trench and fracture zone were parts of one and the same structure and it formed the western and southern boundaries of the Fiji Plateau. Harry Hess and others had suggested that island arcs and trenches are similar to wrinkles produced where the earth's crust is shortened by compression. The sea floor spreading hypothesis extends this suggestion and states that the oceanic crust created at midocean ridges is destroyed at island arcs. We may visualize the oceanic crust as a thin block forming part of a crust of cold tar floating on a lake of hot pitch. If the block moves, the crust in front is folded and wrinkled, and if the leading edge of the block is thrust downward, it melts away because of the heat. At the back edge of the moving block, the crust is first stretched and then breaks and hot pitch moves upward and cools to form new crust. At the sides, the block moves past the crust on each side along what geologists call tear faults. If the New Hebrides Trench is in a zone of compression we would thus expect tear faults connected to the ends and more or less perpendicular to the trench. The Hunter fracture zone is in just the right position and makes just the right connection to be such a tear fault for the New

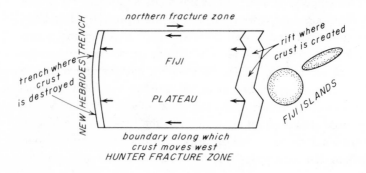

Hebrides Trench. A similar zone of fracturing exists at the northern end of the New Hebrides structure. By analogy, the block of the earth's crust bounded by the New Hebrides Trench and the two fracture zones has moved toward the trench. The block with such boundaries is the Fiji Plateau. Again by analogy, the eastern side of the plateau might be expected to show signs of stretching. We have already seen that the region near Fiji has been broken into mountainous blocks of the ridge and rift type produced elsewhere by stretching. As far as topography can indicate, the hypothesis of crustal drift in this region looks very attractive. "But where," you properly say "is the critical test?" Where indeed? Still the original hypothesis said merely that the island arc and trench formed in an area of compression. From that one could predict the tear faults which have been found at the ends. Given the compression and the tear faults one could predict the stretching and it, or something resembling it, has been observed. It seems that topography can do little more. What are needed are other types of observations.

On 1 August, after many and many a delay for weather we began again to measure heat flow and take a few cores of sediment just south of the Hunter fracture zone. On successive days we obtained values of 0.1, 0.1, and 0.3 heat flow units, all far below normal. Our simple model appeared to be realized. Heat flow was very high on the high plateau (1½ miles deep but high compared to most of the sea floor), heat flow was low in and near the fracture zones bounding the plateau. The topographic and heat flow provinces coincided and with a high degree of probability had related origins. A very happy result. The wild surmise of three weeks before had been tested with an average of one heat flow measurement a day and it was correct. The Fiji Plateau has the highest heat flow of any known large area on earth and the hot area is confined to the plateau. Gentlemen parachutists take heart. Now we can wonder why the plateau has high heat flow.

The sediment core we took near one of the heat probes was not without interest. It contained pebbles made of soft mud containing microorganisms 10 million to 15 million years old. Soft mud pebbles cannot be transported more than a trivial distance without breaking up so we had the evidence of a slump from an adjacent submarine volcano. The microfossils showed that the sediment that slumped was first deposited on the volcano many millions of years ago. We now had converging lines of evidence that this fracture zone was relatively inactive. Both the northern and southern borders of the Fiji Plateau are largely without earthquakes and now at both borders we had found that the volcanoes generally are old. The junction or transition between the New Hebrides Trench and Hunter fracture zone has quite different characteristics. Earthquakes are abundant, and volcanoes are active. Was the trench a rejuvenated feature now forming along a more ancient zone of weakness? This would bear looking into.

By 3 August we were ready for a further assault on the edge of the Fiji Plateau. At last we had weather that was suitable or at least not impossible, and we were over a steep-sided ridge which appeared to be a fault block which should expose the truncated deep layers of the crust of the plateau. What would they be? Several dredge hauls later we knew no more than before. We dredged volcanic rock but on board ship we had no way of knowing its age nor its chemical composition. We really could not be sure whether the ridge was a faulted remnant of the edge of the plateau or merely a volcano of similar form. Oh for some information on the structure of the crust! Perhaps we could get it on a later leg of the expedition.

We took another heat flow on the plateau to the northwest of the ridge and got another extraordinarily high value, ho hum. Then it was off the plateau for the last time in this leg, across the fracture zone, and on to a new problem. A few days earlier it occurred to me that our teaching program on the expedition was flawed. We were teaching the students how to survey submarine topography, stand scientific watches, take cores and dredge, measure heat flow, and live on an oceanographic expedition. What we were not doing was teaching anybody how to manage expedition operations. In fact we had never taught anybody how to run an expedition since our general procedure was evolved in the early 1950s. Some people had a knack for it and ran expeditions and some didn't. Usually a student was chief scientist only when he was lucky enough to be working with a small group of fellow students and friends on his own thesis problem. No one ever ran a ship with a teacher watching the operations. A "chief scientist of the day" was forthwith appointed for the next three days and three students were successively in charge of operations. It seemed to work very well. Dave Johnson, Clem Chase, and Warren Smith buckled down to meshing all the various operations on the ship into a practicable yet flexible program for a day. Dave was first and he raised the question of whether he was just supposed to make sure that the ship carried out the program of sounding and sampling already outlined or whether he had some free time to do something of his own choice. This matter had not been considered and yet one of the main functions of a chief scientist is to recognize and exercise optional uses for ship time. He was given twenty-two hours to carry out the specific plans of the expedition and two hours to do whatever seemed most fruitful to him. That may not sound like much optional time, but it is sufficient to take a heat flow, or a gravity core, or survey along twenty-two extra miles of track. Thus he could try to add additional information about a wide range of problems. The two hours of additional time also would cost $250 for the ship—which is about what a graduate student earns in a month.

Everything went very well. Each of the students made mistakes but they were of such a nature as to reveal that no other method of teaching would work. I woke up one morning and went to the laboratory to see how Clem Chase was doing in surveying a seamount. We looked at his plot of soundings along the dead reckoning track and he explained what he was trying to do. I asked him what had caused him to make a certain course change, and he said that at that time he had known that he should do something, had tried the course change, and then had known that he should have done something else. When I arrived he had just started to do the something else, which was rapid enough self-teaching to justify the method.

Having apprentice chief scientists had another major benefit as far as I was concerned. I did my best to give the students freedom of action. Consequently when the incident above occurred, Clem had not been to sleep for thirty hours and I was rested and ready to work at something other than hour-to-hour operations. I looked at our profiles and soundings in the vicinity of the New Hebrides Trench, seeking clues about its history. You may recall that I had collected unpublished French soundings while I was in Noumea in December. These were now compiled on our sounding sheets along with our own and other sources. The new French data were of excellent quality and most revealing. They showed a smooth fan spreading east and northeast from the Loyalty Islands toward the New Hebrides Trench. This fan was surely the typical wedge of mud and sand deposited around large islands. It was distinctive, in that it leveled out as it approached the trench. Had an older sediment fan been cut by a newly forming trench? So it appeared, but an alternate possibility existed. Adjacent to many trenches is a low ridge. If one was parallel to the New Hebrides Trench it would form a dam to the sediment fanning out from the Loyalty Islands. When the dam was filled by the sediment, it would produce topography very like what was observed. But if that was the sub-bottom structure, the trench and damming ridge were at least as old and probably older than the sedimentary fan that was dammed. Here was an age relationship that could be established if we had a sub-bottom profile. Perhaps we could get one on the next leg of the expedition.

Meanwhile, we were preparing to dredge the seamount surveyed by Clem Chase who had shrewdly grasped one of the little-known fringe benefits of being a chief scientist and had named it after his wife "June Seamount." We dredged it and two other seamounts to the north, and Ned Allison identified Eocene to Miocene shallow-water fossils although the dredge hauls were from depths of 1200 to 2400 feet. This is the great advantage of having an expert aboard. The results immediately mean something. While we were still dredging the last of the seamounts we knew that they had been islands or very shallow banks at various times from about 10 million to at least 40 million years ago. We also knew that since then they had sunk to their present depths.

The Loyalty Islands to the north lie along the same trend as these seamounts and have had a related history. By studying the islands we can understand much about the seamounts. The largest island, Mare, is 20 by 25 miles in area and appears generally flat when seen from a distance. A central plain 150 to 200 feet high is bordered by a rim 100 feet higher and 1000 to 1500 feet wide. The whole island is limestone except for a small hill of volcanic rock in the middle. It was a volcanic island in Miocene time and was then covered with limestone which formed a very large shallow lagoon—now the plain—surrounded by shallow banks or islands—now the low rim. William Morris Davis, the great American geomorphologist of the early twentieth century, thought that this was such a perfect example of an uplifted atoll that it should be used for drilling to test Darwin's hypothesis of atoll development. Lifu is an L-shaped island 25 by 35 miles and with a central limestone plain at about 100 feet and in many places a rim about 100 feet higher. Fossil reef corals occur in the rim but the rocks under the plain are like those of modern atoll lagoons. The northernmost of the main islands, Uvea, is about the same size and has a similar shape, but only the rim is elevated more than 200 feet above the water. The central plain characteristic of the other two islands is here below water; that is, the ancient Miocene lagoon is also a modern lagoon. Farther north are the Astrolabe Reefs, with a shallow platform about the same size as the large islands, but only a few small, low islands are above sea level.

The Loyalty Islands are in the central part of a line of submarine peaks at least 600 miles long, and the seamounts we had been dredging lie at the southern end. The islands are composed of Miocene limestone uplifted 200 to 300 feet and we dredged similar rock from the seamounts but at depths of 1200 to 2400 feet. All of these prominences were near sea level as shallow limestone banks perched on submarine volcanoes at about the same time. Since then the central ones have gone up and the southern ones down. What happened to the north? There we have a clue from one of *Argo's* discoveries reported to us by radio. Along the same line as the Loyalty Islands she found a high peak with a top that was flat except for slightly

elevated edges. In short a typical drowned atoll in shape but
with the reef rim at a depth of 3900 feet. If this drowned atoll
is, as it appears to be, related to the Loyalty Islands, then sub-
sidence has occurred on a far greater scale to the north than
to the south. If this long line of ancient islands has been partially elevated and partially depressed, we might expect that
similar effects would be observable elsewhere in the region.
Perhaps they are. The 250-mile-long island of New Caledonia
is parallel to the Loyalty Islands. It has been elevated in the
center and its ends have been depressed. The depression is
indicated by the formation of great reefs which rise above
shallow lagoons extending additional hundreds of miles along
the trend of the islands. Thus this whole region of Melanesia
has been elevated in the center and has sunk along the northern
and southern margins. Here was one more in a sequence of very
complicated events in the geological history of Melanesia.

We completed our survey and dredging of the northernmost of three seamounts by obtaining a position by radar on
Walpole Island, our dependable if invisible beacon. We wanted
to see it but the possibility of discovering another suspected
fracture zone took first priority on our time. We had had
extraordinary good fortune in such discoveries so far. The first
bathymetric map we compiled of Melanesia was done in part
by students at Scripps and in some areas was based on scanty
and unreliable soundings. It showed the northern edge of the
platform of the Loyalty Islands and New Caledonia as a vague
undulating declivity dropping into a nondescript basin. This
was the edition available when Jerry Winterer took *Argo*
through the Coral Sea on Leg II of *Nova*. Since then we had
made a new map incorporating the soundings obtained from
unpublished data accumulated by French and Australian
oceanographers and hydrographers in the region. I have already mentioned the value of the French sounding lines between New Caledonia and the New Hebrides in connection
with the age of an apron of sediment east of the Loyalty
Islands. Additional lines suggested the existence of a very
linear fracture zone trending east-west and bounding the
platform. "Suggested" may be a little strong. This was a matter of rather arbitrarily discarding some of the conflicting

sounding lines and retaining others on the basis that it was then possible to draw a map similar to maps drawn elsewhere in the world where good data were adequate to draw a good map. On this hunch our map was modified to show a fracture zone of ridges and troughs trending east-west and bounding the northern edge of the New Caledonia–Loyalty platform. We brought copies of the new edition of the map to Suva in late June and Jerry and I discussed this doubtful feature. Bad weather and delays caused him to take *Argo* off the Fiji Plateau and sail toward the Gulf of Papua during Leg IV. That was just at the time when on *Horizon* we were realizing that the plateau probably had very high heat flow and that we would have to make up the heat flow measurements that *Argo* could not make. Jerry was engaged in the constant exercise of the chief scientist on an oceanographic ship, namely trying to identify and solve problems with maximum efficiency. He observed that his general track to the Gulf of Papua would take him along the trend of this supposed fracture zone and resolved to test its existence while he could do it with hardly any expenditure of ship time. He modified the *Argo* course and found the fracture zone on his first pass through the area. Nine more crossings were more accurately aimed as the trend and character of the zone were resolved. The mapping continued from time to time in the next few weeks, and it developed that the fracture zone, named "d'Entrecasteau" after the nearby reefs, marks an important fault.

Heartened by this success, we set out from our dredging to seek a suspected fracture zone south of New Caledonia. Why was it suspected? Because sounding lines were conflicting in the area and if one line was arbitrarily accepted and another arbitrarily rejected, the map would show a deep trough just south of New Caledonia. This trough would lie on a line between the Hunter fracture zone and some other suspected fracture zones further west. We did not modify our base map in this area to show such a trough but it certainly was worth seeking. Appropriate courses were laid out to confirm or deny the trough and we awaited developments. It turned out to be one of the smoothest regions we had seen in all of Melanesia. There was no trough at all, nothing but a few gullies about fifty feet deep. By this time we were too close to Noumea, our next port, to turn east for further dredging. It was too shallow for a heat flow measurement that would mean anything. We did not have enough time before our estimated arrival in port to sail to deep water. We could have spent a few hours surveying off the entrance to the reef off Noumea. However, considering the existence of an oceanographic laboratory and fully equipped ship at Noumea, this seemed rather pointless or even discourteous. We headed into port.

# Leg V  Noumea and Nearly Back

**CHAPTER NINE** The Bulari Passage off New Caledonia is one of the loveliest passes on earth as the ship enters between breaking reefs and heads toward a tiny island with a great white lighthouse. It was the first land our ship approached when I first crossed the Pacific in 1942, and I felt nostalgic. Judging by their photos and sketches and hungry looks, my shipmates on *Horizon*, or at least the younger ones, will remember it equally well twenty-five years from now. Once inside the reef, it was not safe to continue to stream our long cables in shallow water, so we suspended the scientific watch as the ship stopped to pick up a pilot. Being practically in port, although several hours from land, it seemed appropriate to have a symposium on what we had achieved. Since a symposium is a wine-drinking party with discussions, we drank California champagne in the laboratory. The atmosphere was congratulatory and festive but underneath perhaps a little tired. The crew of *Horizon* had not been long at sea but, in a nautical sense, it had had a rough time and needed rest and recreation.

Thanks to the friendly oceanographers and geologists of Noumea, we had lots of recreation, if little rest, during the next few days. We had two field trips to view the local geology, particularly the parts related to the marine geology of the surrounding region. I went one day to see the great mountains of dunite, peridotite, and serpentine which are so rare in most

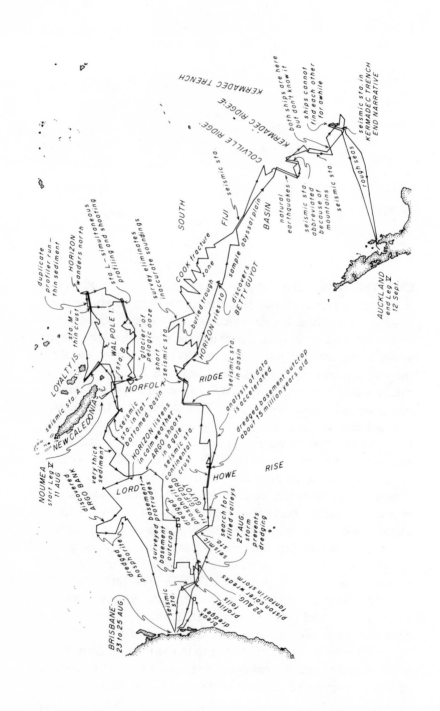

parts of the world but so common in New Caledonia. These are the types of dark green rocks, rich in iron and magnesium, which probably form the mantle and crust under the ocean. If Hess is right, the difference between the oceanic crust and mantle is merely that the crustal rocks contain more water. If several geologists are right, these rocks in New Caledonia were once oceanic crust and upper mantle which have been squeezed or thrust up onto New Caledonia in a thin slice. What an opportunity, to climb into a bus and step out on the erstwhile crust of the ocean basin! If only we could be certain that these rocks were oceanic crust, what a lot of effort could be saved at sea, but this is prevented by a geological "uncertainty principle." The oceanic crust can be unambiguously identified only where it is under an ocean and cannot be sampled. Unlike the uncertainty principle of physics, this limitation is not theoretical but practical. Given new technology, the certified oceanic crust can be sampled.

The mountains of southeastern New Caledonia are an eerie sight. Everything is wrong. The fresh rock is dark green, but it weathers to a very thick orange-red soil, and the familiar earthy browns are totally lacking. The peculiar minerals of these peculiar rocks contain many metallic elements in concentrations that are poisonous to almost all plants. The very great rainfall, however, manages to dilute the poisons, and a sparse and scraggly grey forest, without underbrush, dots the red soil. Combined with the occasional vistas of lush plantations on other types of soil and the distant blue sea and sparkling reefs, the New Caledonia scene deserves a painter.

In addition to seeing the oceanic crust as others see it, we had the ordinary tidying and planning to keep the expedition going. George Shor replaced Jerry Winterer as a chief scientist and brought with him a large amount of new gear and supplies. We also stocked up on the usual fuel and water, plus bread, cheese, and other foodstuffs for which France is famous even overseas. Indeed, some of our French students purchased their own supplies to take back to La Jolla so they could supplement the local diet of abalone and nutburgers. We brought charts up to date, and Shor and I agreed that we should grossly revise our seismic refraction program. By late

July, I realized that Winterer and Helsley would not be able to measure crustal structure in all the planned places on the Fiji Plateau, and nowhere in the vicinity of New Caledonia. Consequently, we were faced with the possibility that we would not even collect the right information to attempt to solve the main problems of the expedition. I radioed Shor in La Jolla and outlined some changes in plan, and these we had just agreed upon. The general plan for Leg V was to operate the two ships more or less in company and measure crustal structure from Noumea to the Tasman Basin, east of Australia, and then turn southeast and continue the measurements to Auckland. The storms we had been experiencing caused us to change the Tasman-Auckland track from a straight line to a dogleg so we would do the difficult work as far north of the storm belt as possible and then dash down to Auckland. The dogleg took us right by Norfolk Island which was economical of time because we were going there anyway. We had made a second modification of plans in order to fill in the Fiji Plateau information gap. From Norfolk we would turn north in a great loop that would provide information on a variety of problems and give several critical measurements of crustal thickness. It would also put us near Suva in case *Horizon* was running short of fuel on what would be a long leg, or in case some critical equipment needed repairs. In sum, it all seemed quite reasonable, and we picked tentative sites for the seismic stations and designated them with letters so we could talk about them by radio.

In Noumea I transferred from *Horizon* to *Argo* after Winterer and Helsley had vacated the chief scientist's cabin and in order to make the chief scientist's cabin on *Horizon* available for George Shor. A comparison of these two cabins will give some indications of the differences in life on the two ships. The one on *Horizon* contains two bunks, one above another, a bench, a Navy-type metal desk with drawers for clothes below, a wash basin, and a closet. There are two fans, an air vent, and no portholes. Repeated cleanings have little effect because of the amount of greasy dust circulated by the air vents. The desk is usually useless because the ship pitches too much to permit sitting beside it. The nearest toilet is shared with eight other people and is two doors away. The cabin on *Argo* also has two bunks one above another but there the resemblance ends. The room is about twice as large as on *Horizon* and it has three portholes, one forward and two on the side. It contains adequate storage for clothes, a low table, an easy chair, a normal desk and chair, and a wash basin. It has a connecting door to a toilet and shower shared only with the captain, who has an adjacent cabin. The desk is usable and I even feel safe in leaving a typewriter on it, although of course I tie it with bungee cord to the light stand which is screwed to the top of the desk. The easy chair and table and desk chair are also tied in place, although they will stay put without tying if the weather is not too rough.

All this stability, at least compared to *Horizon*, results because *Argo* is of a reasonable size. She is 213 feet long, 39½ feet in beam, has a draft of about 15 feet, and displaces a little over 2000 tons when full. This is about the displacement, although not the proportions, of a naval destroyer. She was built by the Basalt Rock Company of Napa, California in 1944, the same vintage wartime year as *Horizon*, and is getting old. She has numerous laboratory and office spaces, mess halls, and a lounge, in which the crew of thirty-three and scientific staff of ten to twenty are dispersed. As a consequence the atmosphere is very different from the coziness of *Horizon* even though the same people move from one ship to the other. This is a more professional ship but also a colder one.

The morning of 11 August we had the ships side by side and transferred all the samples and equipment from the *Horizon* explosives magazine to *Argo* and loaded it with about 12 tons of Nitramon from the crib on the bow of *Argo*. By afternoon, everything was in place and we left again for Bulari Pass and Leg V. The ships, operating for the first time in concert, immediately separated to minimize duplication of data and headed by different courses to a rendezvous the next morning. On the way we were profiling, and for the first time I watched the unfolding of the fantastic records which the system was now producing. In many places and for hours on end we could see the structures under the sea floor as easily as we could see the floor under the sea water. We could see folded and faulted sedimentary layers buried under hundreds to thousands of feet of sand and mud. We could trace deep, steep-sided troughs under a perfectly smooth abyssal plain. I felt something like a mariner who has groped his way into a foggy port year after year and one day is presented with a radar set and can see through the fog. It all seemed so easy. Marine geologists have had to present diversified and cogent arguments why abyssal plains are places where horizontal sedimentary layers have buried older hills. These newer records simultaneously showed the flat plain, the horizontal layers under the surface, and the hills under the layers. Everything was now obvious. How would we have any fun any more? What problems would require any thinking? Well, the first thing we noticed was that we could not only see the hills under the plains but also the internal structure under the hills, and no one had ever been able to say much about such structures. We soon saw that relatively transparent sediment occurred in most places just under the sea floor and it varied in thickness in complex ways. We observed that the "basement," a term meaning the deepest thing you can see with a given instrument, had had a complex history which presumably could be unraveled. We found, as others had before us, that we could direct our bottom sampling with far more intelligence because we could see whether we had flat, young sediment under the ship, or older folded rocks which had emerged through the sediment and were exposed at the sea floor. The profilers, therefore, were not going to reduce deep sea geology to routine. Like so many newly developed instruments and techniques, they would merely make the answers to the old problems obvious, and in turn expose a whole new group of mysteries. And what of the American institutions and ships without the latest profilers? They would have to acquire them or drop out of some kinds of research. And what of the small oceanographic institutions in the less affluent countries which had not yet acquired even precision echo sounders or magnetometers or temperature probes? The young men may join the brain drain simply because they are trained to do research and at home they cannot possibly get access to proper but expensive equipment.

We met at Seismic Station A on a great plain, 6600 feet deep, between New Caledonia and the Loyalty Islands. We could not see them but the islands were detectable at the limit of radar and as we constantly plotted data on maps we could sense them around us. I suppose that George Shor and his associates have done at least a hundred seismic stations at sea, and I probably have been partially involved in fifty. My general reaction to the first one in this series was that the level of confusion had not noticeably decreased. A station is a complex series of events. First, one ship has to arrive at a previously agreed place in the trackless ocean. Then it streams three cables, each a thousand or more feet long, which include the hydrophones which detect pressure waves in sea water. The streaming is done by letting the cables float in place while the ship drifts away under the influence of the wind. The appropriate recorders being operational, the "listening ship" is ready. Meanwhile, the "shooting ship" is positioning itself about ten miles away from where it thinks the agreed-upon point is. There may ensue a complicated, acrimonious, and sterile discussion because, considering the inaccuracy of celestial navigation, the ships never agree on where they are even when they are side by side. This occurred at Station A because the navigators on the ships had been told to go to a certain latitude and longitude, or ten miles from it, respectively, and they spent considerable time in a curious sort of blind mating dance.

*Argo* was shooting and Dale Newhouse was by the shooting bench. Cached at appropriate distances around him and around the ship were the fuse lighters, caps, and charges for the half-pound to 300-pound explosions. In the laboratory and on a radio circuit with *Horizon* and with Dale were various people connected with the operation. Most active was Dan Karig, who was running the firing circuit. On *Horizon* were George Shor, in charge of this far-flung empire, and Baron Thomas operating the hydrophone streamers, recorders, and radio.

At last, all was ready; we put a small shot into the water to test the system before beginning the actual shooting run. Perhaps all was not quite ready. One hour and forty minutes later the receiving system on *Horizon* was capable of detecting a test shot, and we started to move straight toward her. Next, we passed her on the side away from the hydrophone cables so we would not cut them and proceeded forty miles in a straight line dropping larger and larger charges at longer and longer intervals as we sped away. "Sped" may seem a little grandiose for a forward motion of 12 knots, but speed is an essential of the shooting run. The charges have a fuse that delays the explosion by about a minute to allow them to sink to where most of the energy will go into the water rather than up into the air. The biggest charges have the shortest fuses. At 12 knots we go about a thousand feet in a minute, and the big charges make the ship ring like a very large bell. The seamen, who spend so much time chipping and painting the decks, occasionally attest that the big charges crack and flake the thick paint. At 6 knots, the explosion would be roughly four times as intense, and if we suddenly stopped we would blow off the fantail. So, within our limited capabilities, we sped along. Then our roles were reversed. We stopped and streamed hydrophones. *Horizon* pulled in hydrophone streamers and prepared to fire a test shot and then duplicate our shooting run. It was not quite ready to speed along, however. It was not quite ready even to move and two hours passed before the floatabout was ended and the main engines were operational. In 1950, when he was developing these techniques for Scripps, Russ Raitt declared that the only weaknesses in the system were not connected with the experimental hydrophones and electronics but with the radios and the ships. Nothing has changed.

Our listening is centered in the seismic "doghouse," which is a small house trailer rigged as an electronics center. It was welded to the deck on the fantail at the start of *Nova*, and it will be removed and hauled back to Scripps when the ship returns to La Jolla. Meanwhile, it is a snug little scientific castle containing Helen Kirk and Duffy McGowan. The girls ordinarily do all the receiving together and Helen analyzes the results from both ships because we have the only computer. Hour after hour they go through a complex routine of recording and communicating with *Horizon* and analyzing to see

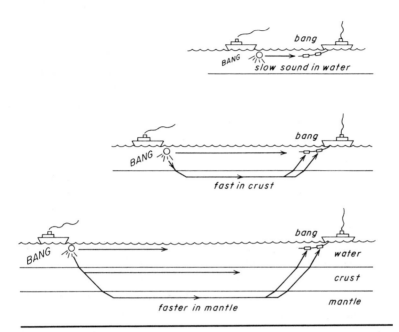

what is happening and thus what should be done next. The energy of the explosion goes in all directions and is refracted as it moves into the deeper layers of the crust which have higher velocities of propagation. The principal signal detected in the doghouse is the time of arrival of the first pressure wave, regardless of its path. It may be useful to visualize a cross-country auto race along roads with quite different speed limits. If the race is short, the car which follows the most direct path will win, even though the speed limit is low. So the first energy from the charges dropped near the ship arrives directly through the water on a reasonably straight line. However, to return to the race, if the goal is a hundred miles from the start, the fastest route may be to go some distance out of the way to a freeway with a higher speed limit. If it is a thousand miles away, the freeway route is a certain winner. So the first arriving energy from the more distant explosions follows a devious path into the depths of the crust and the top of the mantle. By running a whole series of road races of different lengths and assuming everyone always goes the speed limit, it would be possible to determine both the different speed limits and the different distances traveled within each speed limit. Such a determination is made in a seismic refraction station to measure the structure of the crust. In an elegant operation, the shots are economically spaced to yield the maximum information for a minimum time and quantity of explosives. Duffy sits in the doghouse wearing a sweatshirt with the cartoon dog Snoopy on the front and a large sign on the back saying "I've got to start acting more serious—tomorrow."

The important consideration in a seismic station is to keep shooting until the first energy received is traveling through the mantle. Then, in due course, the velocity and layer structure of the crust can be worked out. For two-ship work this requires the transfer of data from ship to ship by rope and radio. With frequent stations the results take some time to analyze. Consequently, I shall have to return to the crustal structure a little later when all the western stations are done. Meanwhile Station A has a crust of thickness intermediate between a continent and an ocean basin—which is not very startling considering that the depth is also intermediate. The sediment is thick but that is also expectable because it usually is thick under an abyssal plain.

During the course of the shooting and listening we had been absorbing the potentialities of the profilers on the two ships and our interest returned to the age and history of the fan of sediment shown by French soundings east of the Loyalty Islands, the fan that appeared to be cut by the New Hebrides Trench. By going from Station A to Station M on the Fiji Plateau we might make two profiler crossings of the fan and of the western edge of the plateau. Shor was agreeable and at the end of the station *Horizon* turned east. *Argo* went southeast to duplicate the seismic run with an air-gun profile. This was a new development. The profiling had never been done during the shooting runs because records were unobtainable at shooting speed. Moreover, it seemed probable that the shots would damage the hydrophone streamers. Duplicating the shooting run took six hours, and I began to realize that no time was allotted for this purpose and that if we did it at every station we would have to have fewer stations or eliminate most of our

dredging and surveying. This was something that would need
to be improved or we were in trouble. The air-gun record was
a beautiful thing, about 3000 feet of finely layered sediment
without visible bottom lay under the abyssal plain. For millions of years nothing had interrupted the quiet filling of this
basin. At last, we turned east and for the third time were
headed toward Walpole Island, our natural radar beacon.
This time it was day, and we could at last pass close by and
see it. Unfortunately, most of the people who had been involved with Walpole Island were still on *Horizon*, now a hundred miles to the north. Only Warren Smith and I knew it as a
steadfast pip on a radar screen. Even so, everyone seemed to
find it interesting as we approached. It was just as described
in the *Sailing Directions*, vertical walls, flat top, and surrounded
by a mist of breaking surf. However, a geologist's eye could
also see different layers of limestone exposed in the great cliffs
and forming a few steps where the softer rock had been eroded
rapidly. It looked just like the descriptions of the Loyalty Islands to the north except it was so small, and it also looked
very like the guyots that we had dredged to the south. All
along this chain, limestone which was formed just below sea
level had since been uplifted into islands or depressed into
guyots. This was a marked contrast to the quiescence indicated by the smooth flat sedimentary layers of the basin next
to the chain. The history we were trying to unravel was going
to be complicated.

Once again we approached the trench but armed as
never before. Once again we left the trench trailing bits of
confetti—a chewed-up paper tiger. We penetrated a few thin
pockets of sediment between the Loyalty Islands and the
trench, but it developed that we were too far south to cross the
Loyalty fan. *Horizon*, which was at just the right position to
study the sub-bottom structure of the fan, did not manage to
operate its arcer. On the eastern side of the trench, where it
forms the boundary of the Fiji Plateau, the air-gun did not
penetrate at all. Bedrock without perceptible structure lay at
the bottom except for an occasional sediment patch ten to fifty
feet thick. We were verifying and extending the earlier obser-

vations of Chase and Winterer that the Fiji Plateau is almost bare of recent or even old sediment—rock yes, mud and ooze, no.

Horizon was waiting for us at Station M and we came shooting. Then we listened in our turn, and finally we got under way and duplicated the track along the shooting run to make an air-gun profile. The aggregate took much more time than we had available and we simply had to do something to speed up the seismic station procedure. We decided to try to combine the air-gun and shooting runs.

Horizon finished shooting and then absentmindedly turned north for an hour before someone discovered a navigation point had been misplotted. We spend so much time in northern latitudes and western longitudes that the plotting of points in southern latitudes and eastern longitudes requires the same constant attention that an American devotes to driving on the left side in England. Finally, both ships turned south and made a last crossing of our old acquaintance, the Hunter fracture zone. Down the great roller coaster we went again, trailing more streamers than before and bouncing sound of all frequencies off the rocky pinnacles below. We found sediment only near Hunter Island where it might be expected because of the fall of volcanic ash. Of the hoped-for evidence of exposed layers at the edge of the Fiji Plateau there was none.

How different it was once we left the plateau—sediment was everywhere. The deep trough in the center of the fracture zone was buried under a thousand feet of flat-lying mud and ooze. Further south, a similar amount lay under the two-mile deep floor of the South Fiji Basin but its origin appeared different. The sediment was finely layered and appeared to be draped over the low hills in the basement. This is the standard criterion for recognizing sediment which has fallen particle by particle from the overlying water. The alternative means of emplacing it is by muddy currents flowing along the bottom and these are unable to rise over even low hills. Consequently, they deposit sediment around hills which ultimately are buried.

The fallout of "foram ooze" consists of the microscopic shells of one-celled organisms, chiefly Foraminifera, which live in the surface waters. Because they float and drift about in the ocean, they are called "pelagic." They are white and the fallout has been compared quite accurately with a slow but constant snowfall. The ooze rarely accumulates faster than a half inch to two inches per millennium and thus the "snowfall" is invisible even to the fish who swim through it. The thickness we could detect with the air-gun probably represents the accumulation of roughly 25 million years of pelagic snow. Fifty miles away is the Fiji Plateau which has little or no covering of ooze, and yet pelagic organisms live in the waters above it and fall to the bottom—as we know from our cores. Where are the snows of 25 million yesteryears?

It was time for the shooting run on Station L, the run with the air-gun going. The explosives are dropped from the port side of the ship so we hauled in the gun from that side to prevent accidental snagging. That left one air-gun and the hydrophone streamer to starboard. The half-pound charges had no effect on the gun or streamer, and we could see the sub-bottom spread out under us during the seismic run. This would give much better records for final interpretation because our duplicate runs were never along exactly the same track as the shooting runs. So far, we were improving our technique but how would the hydrophone streamer react to larger charges? Five pounds and then sixteen pounds had no effect but the larger charges have shorter fuses and would explode closer to the ship. We calculated the 50-pounders would only double the intensity of the shock on the hydrophones but that 188-pounders would increase it twenty-fourfold. Realizing that if we damaged the hydrophone streamer, we might not be able to repair it and had no replacement, most of the scientists wanted to haul in the hydrophones before the larger charges were exploded. Realizing that we might not damage it and we might repair it, we went ahead. The ship rang and the paint jumped but the hydrophone streamer was as serene as a well-fed water snake. At the next station we were dropping 300-pound charges past the hydrophones without a care in the world. *Horizon*, while listening, measured the heat flow at the southern edge of the Hunter fracture zone and obtained 0.8 units, which was another low value like the three obtained nearby during the previous leg. When we stopped to listen we

measured 1.1 heat flow units, which is closer to normal, but
then we were closer to the broad and deep and normal South
Fiji Basin. In geophysics, a region which is normal in one way
is often normal in all. The seismic refraction obtained a complete cross section of the crust and it was clear that it was
relatively thin and thus normal for a deep oceanic station. The
sediment seemed thicker than usual but more complete analysis would have to wait until Helen Kirk had the data from
*Horizon.*

If the water had been removed at Station L, we would
have seen a giddy two miles below a very gently rolling
plain stretching north to a deep trough and beyond it the
endless expanse of the rocky Fiji Plateau rising 4000 feet
above the basin. To the west, where we next would travel, the
view would be a little misty because we didn't know much
and some of the things reported were doubtful. Ahead about
200 miles was the great Norfolk Ridge trending north-south
and about 12,000 feet high and relatively flat on top, like the
Sierra Nevada. Between this great mountain range and the
plain were many foothills and border ranges, but we knew
little about them except where we had *Nova* reconnaissance
lines. Like the mountain men evaluating the reports of per-
fidious redskins, we headed for the foothills indicated by questionable and conflicting echo soundings.

Our two ships helped blaze a trail west, but we found
that the border ranges were too complex to be mapped in detail in the time we had available. Nevertheless, our profilers
suggested an astonishing conclusion about these ranges. We
were penetrating a great blanket of pelagic sediment draped
over valleys and hills but tending to fill in the valleys and
thereby reduce the local relief. Even the sediment detectable
with the small energy of the air-gun was 1000 to 3000 feet
thick. When the seismic refraction data were calculated, the
sediment proved far thicker than the air-gun could penetrate.
Thus "basement" in this region is only a reflecting surface
within the sediment. Much of the elevation of this mountainous
area was the result of the accumulation of ooze and mud, and
we seemed to be seeing a high plateau in process of developing. To put the water back in the ocean, it appeared that the

shallowness of the region was owing in considerable part to the snowfall of the pelagic sediment. But why here and not on the Fiji Plateau? The mystery deepened when we reached the Norfolk Ridge. The sediment visible on the air-gun was 2000 to 3000 feet thick but the most peculiar feature was a tongue of ooze perched on the crest of the ridge on top of the normal sedimentary layers evident elsewhere. The shape and location of the tongue were just those that would result if snow collected on a high mountain range and began to spread out as a glacier. I had an uneasy feeling that this snowfall analogy was being carried too far. Nevertheless, the evidence was clear that here on the Norfolk Ridge, the pelagic blanket was collecting in such a way as to make the high get higher rather than filling in the lows. At first, we thought that somehow this might be a tongue of mud deposited by currents spreading out along the bottom from New Caledonia to the north but more crossings ruled this out. We were driven to the conclusion that somehow the forams and their friends living in the shallow surface waters could sense the position of the ridge and fall on it, or possibly they were being swept away elsewhere and somehow collected in windrows on the crest of the ridge. Either of these possibilities required deep ocean currents, either accelerating and decelerating at the bottom, or welling upward and increasing productivity along the crest of the ridge. We could hope to find more data bearing on the question when we crossed this ridge and the Lord Howe Rise in future weeks.

We began Seismic Station B shooting along the crest of the Norfolk Ridge in a depth of only 3000 to 4000 feet. The rule is that shallow depths lie over thick crust and so we had to shoot for seventy miles and even then we did not penetrate the full thickness of the crust. We reached the limit of the receiving capabilities of the system and almost reached the end of the available ocean because the southern tip of the New Caledonia reef was not far ahead. In the early evening the station was finished except for the routine of hauling in the seismic hydrophone cables and streaming the other cables to get underway. The business of hauling in cables is usually peaceful and enjoyed by all. It takes little thinking but requires about

six people and thus provides a critical mass for pleasant conversation while watching the sunset or sunrise or dodging the
waves on the deck or just enjoying the sea. That evening was
rather different. As the hauling began, Alan Jones discovered
that the cables were all intertwined and could not be retrieved
and placed in the three appropriate boxes without unscrambling. There we were with three cables each about a thousand
feet long and with various floats and hydrophones in a gigantic backlash. After a bit, we developed a system whereby we
could pull the shortest cable through the other two by opening
up loops and having someone walk through. The remaining
mess was more formidable and we could see an endless dish
of spaghetti stretching for 3000 feet in mounds, piles, and
strings about the deck. About an hour after we began, a
drenching rain was falling and we took to foul weather gear.
As the rain slowly soaked through, we developed a sort of
jump rope system for unscrambling. Dan Karig, beard drip-
ping water, held yards of looped cable in his arms and stepped
over the second cable. Duffy and Graham Taylor then picked
up the cable on the deck and passed it over his head like a
jump rope. The rest of us tended loose ends and did preliminary unwinding. Later when we were wetter we had advanced
to what Duffy called "twosies," in which two people held arm-
loads of looped cable and jumped rope. We passed to "three-
sies" before we were done and the whole mess was straightened out. By that time, we were wet, cold, and thoroughly
enjoying ourselves. Slaving and soaking, laughing and joking,
I never had a better time, and we had more people working
at the end than at the beginning.

From the northern end of the Norfolk Ridge, we sailed
northwest down the cliff of the continental slope off New Caledonia and into a great trough 11,000 feet deep and floored
with an abyssal plain. In this New Caledonia Basin we shot
another seismic station and found again a relatively normal
oceanic crust covered with a lot of sediment. It was hard
sediment because we tried unsuccessfully to penetrate it with
a temperature probe, gravity core, and piston core and Horizon made two tries.

# Leg V The Lord Howe Rise

**CHAPTER TEN**   We came next to the Lord Howe Rise, an enigma discovered a century ago and named after the island which rises above it and which in turn is named after the admiral who explored the Pacific before Cook. What is its nature and what has been its history? Why is so much of it at a depth of about 4000 to 5000 feet? These are very odd depths. The continents have an average height only a little above sea level. The ocean basins in general are three miles deep. Intermediate levels are really quite uncommon and almost always occur at the boundary between continents and ocean basins. The Lord Howe Rise, on the other hand, is a relatively isolated, smooth, and flat-topped elevation almost surrounded by deep ocean basins. Moreover, elevation or depth generally is a very reliable indication of crustal thickness and density because the crust floats on the mantle. If it is thick it is a high continent. If it is very thin it is a deep ocean basin. Intermediate thicknesses, like intermediate depths, are rare and of quite uncertain origin. Is the rise a thin continent or a thick ocean basin crust? Is it old and decaying, is it stable, is it young and growing—perhaps by sea floor spreading?

Our reconnaissance phase of the *Nova* Expedition had helped answer some of these questions. As we left the New Caledonia Basin on 18 August we knew that the rise is flat because it is covered with hundreds to a few thousand feet

of more or less flat sediment. Below is a "basement" of folded
and eroded sedimentary rock layers. We also knew that the
basement is exposed in a hole in the blanket or horizontal
sediment west of New Caledonia, where we had no time to go,
and possibly also on the western margin of the rise. Several
crossings showed that this margin is an abrupt cliff as much
as half a mile high, and this appeared to be bare of sediment.
We would be crossing this cliff in at least two places with each
ship, and our plans were built around the expectation that we
could there dredge, core, and survey the basement outcrops.
We also knew of a north-south line of banks and guyots west
of the center of the rise. These we planned to survey and
dredge simply because dredging guyots in the past has been
most profitable. Usually one obtains fossils characteristic of
shallow water which reveal when the guyot was an ancient
island and thus show how fast it has sunk. Another parallel
line of submarine volcanoes and guyots lies further west in the
deep Tasman Basin, and we also planned to dredge these to
see if the two lines are the same age. By comparing these
ages with those of yet other lines of volcanoes far to the east
in Melanesia we might hope to obtain evidence of some sys-
tematic process such as sea floor spreading. We were already
certain that many large faults and lines of volcanoes in Melanesia have a trend almost exactly north-south and thus surely
are related in some way. Probably they were produced by a
single process and at the same or related times. That is, if the
sea floor cracked in many places simultaneously, like a piece
of glass, then all the north-south cracks appeared at about the
same time. This includes the cracks which have channeled hot
lava to the surface and produced the lines of volcanoes. On
the other hand if the faults and volcanoes are produced by sea
floor spreading, then they are the product of the same process
but produced successively in time. If we could find a symmetrical grouping of lines of volcanoes centered around some
rift, such as the New Caledonia Basin, we could take this as
evidence for sea floor spreading.

   To investigate all these problems we had allotted time
for three seismic refraction stations on the rise and several
days for sampling and surveying. As we left the New Cale-

donia Basin, George Shor and I went over plans by radio and agreed to survey toward the first of these stations, shoot it, and then go on our separate ways for five days to survey and dredge the cliffs and guyots in different parts of the rise. Then we would shoot in the Tasman Basin and turn east for the other two stations on the rise. We had no real expectation that ten days later the origin and history of the rise would have become an open book, but our hopes were high.

The first question investigated was the existence of a problematical fracture zone extending east-west from the southern tip of the New Caledonia reef to an apparently faulted offset of the continental slope of Australia. This fracture zone was strongly suggested by a line of soundings 8500 feet deep running along this trend through the Lord Howe Rise, which is only 3600 feet deep in this region. Thus it appeared that a trough a mile deep cut through the crest of the rise, but its shape and even its reality were open to question. It also seemed that the rise changed trend from north-south to north-west at the line of this trough and this gave another suggestion of a great fracture zone with extensive faulting. However, as you will recall, we had already sought this fracture zone where it appeared to truncate the southern end of New Caledonia and had found nothing. Then, however, we had had no air-gun for profiling. Perhaps a trough existed and was buried. This time we were ready for any eventuality.

By the morning of 19 August our survey was well under way. We had made the first zig to get into position and were preparing to make the critical zag that would solve the problem. The weather was as good as the day before. I walked half a mile around the boat deck, eighteen laps per mile, before breakfast and admired the lovely calm sea. We steamed southwest across an abominably dull and smooth sea floor without a trace of a trough. The line of deep soundings was wrong and it appeared that the Lord Howe Rise is continuous with the Chesterfield Platform to the north without any slightest interruption. Moreover we were detecting and then continuously tracing a sub-bottom reflector with the air-gun and it was as smooth as the sea floor but about 2000 feet below it. No faulting or folding had occurred in all the time since the sediment above this basement reflector started to be deposited. The duration of this time was, of course, unknown until we could obtain a sample of the basement. However, even at the relatively rapid rate of an inch in a thousand years, the sediment had been accumulating for about 20 million years and nothing had happened to it during that time. The supposed fracture zone appeared to be a myth, although the change in trend of the bottom relief requires bending or some deformation in this region.

By noon I had walked another half a mile and the sea was so calm and the ship so stable that I could even run a few laps. That was not possible again for some time. We began to get perfectly astonishing air-gun records. At the top was a layer of sediment virtually transparent to sound waves, like an apartment house wall, in which we could see faint layering showing that the sediment was a sequence of materials with slightly different composition or sizes or consolidation. The surface of this pelagic blanket has been sampled in many places and found to be foram ooze. Thus at the present time and for the last few thousand years at least it is known that these tiny shells have been raining down like an eternal snowfall onto the floor of the Lord Howe Rise. Our air-gun profiles and the arcer records simultaneously collected on *Horizon* showed very convincingly that the same process had persisted for millions of years. The lower layers of the pelagic blanket are increasingly distorted but in a very subtle way which is visible only with a large vertical exaggeration. These gentle distortions are like some observed in rocks exposed by erosion on land. A layer that is flat when it is deposited will commonly become slightly wavy if loaded by burial under still more sediment. Presumably this is all that has happened to the lower part of the pelagic blanket as it has gradually been buried.

Below this blanket is the basement, which consists of a variety of folded and faulted sediments, volcanic rock, and other less common types of rock. What we were seeing was a complex basement, clearly faulted, folded, and eroded; individual layers varied in initial thickness indicating that the sea floor had a slope when the layers were deposited. The shape of these layers very strongly suggested that the Lord Howe Rise had existed for some time and was deformed before the pelagic blanket began its quiet fall. The rise had a long history which was suddenly obvious during a few hours of record collecting. The geologists aboard began to weave fantasies and hypotheses for future testing.

We came up to *Horizon* in delightful weather and exchanged records and spare parts by use of a throwing line and floats. With the essential transfers out of the way after much backing and filling, we at last began the seismic run to measure the thickness of the crust of the rise. Continent or ocean basin? Melantis or Melanesian Rise? As we shot and *Horizon* listened we continued to obtain magnificent air-gun profiles. Every five seconds we felt the distant "hrrmp" of the air-gun. At the start of the run, every three minutes we felt the sharper shock of a ½-pound TNT charge going off under water. The radio transmissions required to coordinate the time of firing and receiving the shots somehow still interacted with the air-gun records, and the TNT explosions caused some confusing noise, but hour after hour the sub-bottom was displayed before us with all the fascination of a mystery program on the television.

First we saw more complicated folding in the basement although the top of the basement remained relatively flat. The folds thus had been eroded in a way that usually happens only at or above sea level. The basement surface is now at a depth of more than 5000 feet and buried under 1000 to 1500 feet of sediment. It has sunk a long way and we had another bit of its history to add to the others. A few hours before midnight the basement began to shoal a little and the surface of the sediment began to drop. Between them the pelagic blanket thinned rapidly. Next a sharp peak appeared, replacing the folded sedimentary basement and piercing the blanket. It was our first example of rock available for sampling but, in the midst of the seismic run, we could hardly afford to stop. The thinning of the blanket probably indicates that the seamount (volcano?) existed before much sediment accumulated. The thin shells of Foraminifera can be moved about by very weak ocean currents. However, the currents over most parts of the rise probably are too gentle to produce such movement or else all the pelagic blanket would be washed off into the surrounding deep and quiet waters. A protruding seamount, however, inevitably deflects and accelerates any ocean currents. Thus the depression on each side of the seamount probably results from scouring and nondeposition just like that around a barn in a blizzard. We could not pause to find out.

An hour before midnight I went·to bed to rest for the next stage of the seismic station when we were to stop, listen, and sample the bottom. By midnight I awoke to find myself pitching in a manner more reminiscent of *Horizon* than *Argo*. I was uneasy about all the Nitramon in the unnautical crib on the forward deck of the ship, not that it would explode but it might be washed overboard. I dragged myself over to a forward-looking porthole and watched the crib as the bow surged up and down and spray dashed across the deck. Although it hit the porthole audibly, the spray could cause no damage and green water was not coming over the bow. In this kind of sea the crib was safe. I listened long enough to feel one larger shot go off behind the ship and then returned to sleep.

By 0130 hours Alan Jones woke me to say that he thought that the sea had become too rough for us to stop and listen safely. The safety involves not sinking, but tangling and losing the long hydrophone cables which tend to wind around the hull and particularly the screws. I went down to the laboratory to look at various wind intensity gauges and to inspect the sea. We were in the midst of a gale with 35- to 40-knot winds and about a ten-foot swell. The afterdeck, so peaceful a few hours before, was a shambles. I watched Dale Newhouse get off one more shot in what were clearly marginal conditions and after a brief consultation with Alan Jones, slowed the ship so we could lash equipment in place on the fantail. We determined that if we changed course a little, the shooting bench, where the charges are fabricated with fuses, would be protected enough to finish the shooting run. We talked to *Horizon* which was seventy miles away and found to our mutual astonishment that it was still in balmy weather with light airs and hardly any swell. We had to accept each other's estimates of operating conditions, however, and we called off the second half of the seismic station but agreed to complete the first half. Then we continued to have trouble in the radio circuits, apparently because we had so much salt spray on our antennas. We got under way and put a 300-pound TNT charge into the water only to have a dud because the fuse had become wet. Finally we successfully completed the run with a last shot. At that place and at 2 A.M. we had to make a complete shift in our programs. Our intention was that after this station *Argo* should go north and *Horizon* south and the two meet in the Tasman Basin for the next seismic work. Our radio conversations had been on that basis. Now the seismic station was done and *Horizon* was seventy miles north of *Argo*. I had been wanting to see the reefs of the Chesterfield Island region for over a year but I reluctantly suggested that *Horizon* go north and by 3 A.M. *Argo* was under way south into the swell.

The senior scientists and ship's officers on the upper deck got little sleep although the lucky students and seamen below reported no difficulties the next morning. They must have been tired because before dawn I woke at the feel of a change in the ship's motion and again peered out of my portholes. We were hardly moving and people were scurrying around on the bow. The Nitramon crib had been hit by two great waves over the bow and a few of the siding boards and some Nitramon cans were on the deck. The crib was patched together and we continued on our way at slightly reduced speed.

By midafternoon we changed course to downwind, due west, and conditions became much pleasanter. Despite rain squalls I managed to walk a mile about the deck and followed that with an afternoon nap. Except for bunks, the ship was rather empty that afternoon. One reason was that we were just ready to launch our five days of geological surveying and sampling. We would stop and sample whenever it seemed promising, which meant sleep might be highly irregular for some time. We were trying to be prepared. After dinner on 20 August we turned south toward a nameless and unsurveyed guyot indicated by a group of soundings from the turn of the century. At 2230 hours I started to plot our track and soundings on a scale of four miles to the inch on a standard maneuvering board of the type used by the Navy. We wanted to dredge the guyot and in order to do so it was necessary to map it as we were about to do. We were reasonably sure it existed but we had no reason to believe that the ancient soundings were correctly positioned within a matter of five miles or more. Moreover, lacking a star fix we didn't know where we were. In retrospect it is obvious that we passed east of the guyot and just barely went over the lower slope. At the time it was a toss-up and I gambled that we were west of the guyot. Three course changes and about half an hour later we were on the flat top at a depth of 900 feet. We went about ten miles, coasted down the other side, hauled in all the cables we were trailing, wheeled about, and prepared to dredge just after 3 A.M. Having found the spot and discussed plans with Fred Dixon I went to sleep knowing he would worry about things. A little before 5 I was awakened with news that the dredge was due up momentarily. I never like to miss watching a dredge coming out of the water. In fact almost everything about dredging is exciting. The whole idea of dredging is preposterous. We stop a ship over a spot where we have every expectation that the bottom is irregular solid rock; we then lower a dredge on a steel cable a fraction of an inch thick and a mile or so long and attempt to break the rock without breaking the cable. When dredging it is fun to watch the strain meters register each variation in tension on the cable to see if the dredge is hitting the bottom and if so how hard it is tugging. Rapid signals ("Stop the ship!," "Pay out wire!") are followed by violent maneuvers if the tension builds up rapidly and the working limit of the wire is approached. When the dredge is finally due back at the surface, the success or failure of all these actions can at last be evaluated. We lean over the fantail staring into the water for the first sight. We call out to slow the winch and see the dredge rise through the last few feet of water. The first important bit of information is now at hand—we have not lost the dredge. While the bottom of the dredge is still in the water it is customary to look down inside to see if anything is in it. A moment later this is impossible because the chain and netting of the dredge are balled together and conceal the contents.

This particular dredge definitely contained something but

we could not yet tell what it was. To empty it we had to detach the dredging cable and then attach a hook to the bottom of the chain bag and invert the dredge. Even then the contents did not fall out until the netting, which was voluminous, was cut free from the chain bag and turned inside out. As Fred hauled upward to invert the dredge, I cut the netting free and began to shake the chain and dredge to try to empty out the contents. Suddenly I heard a very odd sound—the contents tinkled when shaken. We never know what to expect in a dredge, but sound effects from the silent world are definitely out of the ordinary. The only other occasion that comes to mind is when a snapping and popping sound came from the dredge. The compressed gas bubbles in a volcanic rock had been stable at the high pressures of the sea floor but at atmospheric pressure they were expanding and popping the rock to pieces. Dale Krause, the discoverer, called the location "Popcorn Ridge." Now we had a tinkling sound. Well, things that tinkle usually break easily and I began to handle the contents with more care even though they had already been wrenched from the sea floor. Out some pieces tumbled on the deck, little slabs of brown glistening rock with the size and shape of large cookies. We collected a boxful and took it into the laboratory for examination as we resumed surveying to find another dredging site. Warren Smith pulverized and dried some of the rock for microscopic examination and we looked at other fragments with a hand lens. The rock was made of foram ooze partially broken into fragments and then the whole mineralized to form a hard rock. I had seen a very similar rock before; it is a bookend in my office made of phosphorite dredged from the shallow banks off Southern California. We improvised some chemical tests but they hardly seemed necessary; the only material remotely like this on oceanic banks is phosphorite.

While the survey continued I strolled around the deck thinking. The ship goes nowhere near as fast as the mind and plotting takes little time so I could keep track of the surveying while enjoying the weather. Phosphorite generally contains 25 to 30 percent phosphate, which is a basic ingredient of commercial fertilizer. One of the major problems in feeding the exploding population of southeast Asia is finding fertilizer. Even Australia and New Zealand, although sparsely peopled, need phosphate. At present Asia and most of the world are supplied from enormous reserves in a few places such as Morocco, Florida, and the northern Rocky Mountain states. Japan, for example, obtains phosphate through the Panama Canal from Florida. The Melanesian region for some time has been supplied with phosphate rock from the tiny uplifted coral islands of Ocean, Nauru, and Makatea as well as numerous minor contributors. Unfortunately the supply on the islands is giving out and the demand is growing. Consequently Australia and New Zealand and other nations with commercial interests are seeking phosphorite on the shallow sea floor. We had just found some on a bank, a very broad bank, which was one of a line of banks, none of which had ever been dredged. Had we chanced upon a phosphate mine just where one was needed?

I think I have made it clear that Scripps oceanographic expeditions do not have immediate economic goals. Most of the staff would think it highly improper to use government money to compete with taxpaying industry which is ready and eager to find mineral resources or fish for a profit. On the other hand we do not think that oceanography is financed just to satisfy our idle curiosity. We assume that the basic research we do will eventually help find minerals or fish or otherwise repay the investment. Nonetheless it can be satisfying, while engaged in the purest research, to stumble on a gold mine— or even a deposit of fertilizer. Is "stumble" the right word? As a result of past oceanographic expeditions, it has been established that the isolated banks of the world commonly have deposits of phosphorite although generally only small amounts. The *Challenger* dredged a little phosphorite on Agulhas Bank south of South Africa. In recent years the department concerned with agriculture in the Republic of South Africa has engaged a ship and made numerous dredgings to try to find large, high-grade deposits of phosphate but with little success. On our *Monsoon* Expedition we dredged phosphorite on the Campbell Plateau, an extensive shallow area east of New Zealand. The Wellington oceanographers have made other dredgings in the region and quite recently an American commercial exploration company has done extensive sampling. This region is a definite prospect for phosphate.

Off Southern California are extensive shallow banks which are coated with phosphorite. The deposits were discovered and first mapped by oceanographers, mainly from Scripps. They contain 29 percent phosphate, which is just below the commercial level at ports in California. Photographs with some of the first experimental underwater cameras showed that the banks are completely covered with slabs of phosphorite, and dredgings suggested more than one layer. The prospect of a commercial deposit was good enough for several companies to invest money in detailed blocking out of reserves and one proceeded to obtain a mining lease from the United States Government. The mining operations began but quickly stopped because the company reported that it was dredging up live naval shells fired past nearby San Clemente Island in the practice bombardments which used to shake California in the days of battleships and cruisers with guns.

Not many guns had been fired in the waters we were dredging so perhaps these might be mineable banks of the greatest importance to the economy of Melanesia. How could we find out? Our first dredge haul had been at 1600 feet on the uppermost slope of the guyot but below the flat top. The next sensible thing would be to dredge the flat top to see if it was covered with phosphorite slabs like the California banks. If so we could then photograph the top taking pictures every few hundred feet for a few miles in order to learn the extent and concentration of the slabs. I thought as I went around the deck that we really were in an excellent position to concentrate an oceanographic armada on the problem if our efforts looked promising. *Horizon* would be dredging a similar bank to the north in just a few hours. It would dredge another the following day. Moreover the United States Coast and Geodetic Survey ship *Oceanographer* on a round-the-world maiden cruise would be through the region within two months and it could dredge and photograph at any depth.

We crossed the top of a guyot, a noble expanse of more than ten miles at a depth of only 930 feet. Down went the dredge and the strain gauge showed little evidence of hitting rock as we dragged the bottom. Up came the dredge, we peered into it from the fantail bucket and saw little. The dredge was inverted and the sample fell on the deck without tinkling. It was a drab-looking light tan material plus a few disgruntled crabs, sponges and prawns. In the laboratory the material was found to be nodules of limestone of a type which forms on shallow banks in warm water. It was harder than normal and had some gradation in color from dark on the outside to very white in the center. The outer part had been phosphatized, which was interesting, but the rock did not appear to be of any commercial value. Perhaps everywhere else on the bank the phosphorite was thick, dark, and glossy, but it seemed unlikely and we felt let down. We could have tried again but *Horizon* would do so on the other two guyots and it seemed that that would be enough. We lashed down the dredge and camera and left the guyot alone in its glory. Within the hour *Horizon* reported that it too had dredged partially phosphatized rock from a guyot in this chain which also had a very broad top at just 900 feet but had found no pure phosphorite. Later dredge hauls by both ships brought up more of the same material. The dream of a sea of tinkling fertilizer was gone but it may be restored if further dredging is more fortunate.

As I was completing the plot of the seamount by adding the soundling line off to the west it occurred to me that after a day of surveying and two dredge hauls the guyot deserved a name. I had already named a seamount off Chile after my wife because I discovered it on her birthday in 1958. However, it was a very small seamount, although the largest found that day, and I thought that a wife who will put up with a husband who goes away for sixteen oceanographic expeditions surely deserved something better. Moreover, it is quite acceptable in international usage to apply the same proper name to different types of geographical features, and a seamount is not the same as a guyot. So "Gifford Guyot" it is, off Australia, to match Gifford Seamount on the other side of the Pacific. While in a naming mood I realized that in the course of our reconnaissance survey we had discovered the northernmost guyot in this same line and that *Horizon* had just dredged it. Having

long since given its name to a guyot and only last month to a
bank, the ship itself was not eligible for providing a name.
The expedition name, however, had not yet been used. Hence
we have "Nova Guyot" just south of the Chesterfield Island
reefs. The middle members of the line have long had names,
but such a group is named after the end members, the "Nova-
Gifford" guyots to which I shall be referring.

During the first hour of 22 August we crossed the boundary cliff between the smooth but mountainous Lord Howe
Rise and the flat plain of the Tasman Basin. We began a survey to find the ideal spot to sample the basement where it
might appear protruding through the blanket of pelagic ooze
—which was still a thousand feet thick in most places but getting thinner in patches. Before breakfast the survey was going
as planned in beautiful weather. I walked a mile about the
deck exchanging greetings with the early risers, contemplating
several days of improvising marine geology, and little dream-
ing of the disasters in store. Slowly but steadily the wind began to rise and the swell to steepen. Not long after lunch we
took a few deep green swells over the bow and again damaged the forward crib containing Nitramon. It could not stand
much more of a beating and we rallied round to transfer explosives after slowing the ship and turning into the weather.
Can by can several tons were moved across the wet and pitching decks and stacked in the protected crib aft. When it was
full we began to stack and secure the cans in the upper laboratory until at last the forward deck was empty. Meanwhile
the deck crew had disassembled the crib so the boards would
not be smashing across the decks, and the bow was clean and
shipshape.

The explosives transfer took over two hours and we
drifted an unknown distance northeast before again starting
to survey to the west. The wind and swell grew more intense
and we were in a dilemma. Even if we could find an ideal
outcrop of basement it was becoming increasingly improbable
that we could successfully or even safely dredge or piston
core. The wind was up to 35 knots with higher gusts and the
swell was rising. We had long since lashed down all the heavy
sampling equipment on the fantail and it was doubtful that it

should be moved about. We could continue to survey, but because of our rendezvous with *Horizon* we had a limited choice of directions. Geologically the most profitable program would be to continue to seek a basement outcrop in a southeasterly direction. But, according to the weather reports, the center of an intense storm lay there. We could go west and dredge a guyot but that should be saved for just before the next seismic station, which was to be near the guyot.

Because of the direction of the weather we continued slowly west to make one more crossing of the boundary cliff before a decision was necessary. Meanwhile I again inspected the pilot charts which indicate the intensity and direction of winds, storms, and swell at different times. Had we made some mistake in scheduling an expedition for this time and place? We had had nothing but stormy weather for most of the two months I had been at sea on *Nova*. No, the charts confirmed that storms were few, hurricanes at a minimum, and expectable wind and swell quite reasonable in Melanesian waters in July and August. This was not only the most convenient time for taking students but also a reasonable one for weather. What was happening? I recalled the approximate words of the King in Thurber's *The White Deer* when his court astronomer told him shooting stars had appeared in the sky. "They throw these things at me," he said. In a democracy we have to remember that the pilot charts deal only with averages.

Several hours later Fred Dixon was climbing down from the boat deck to enter the laboratory by the rear door and looked across the lighted fantail. He came in to announce that the piston core weightstand was rolling about the deck. That meant we had a 1200-pound cylinder of lead, with a short pipe sticking out of each end, rolling about and fully capable of smashing anything it encountered. We immediately slowed the ship and turned on a course to try to protect the fantail from the weather. This meant risking a great tangle of the cables streaming behind the ship, but there was no way to go past the rolling weightstand safely and pull in the cables. Dixon and Francheteau and I went out to snub up the weightstand after a briefing about what we would do. The weightstand was smashing into the corner of the seismic doghouse with each roll and it was going to be difficult to stop it in such a confined place. It made a few more desultory dents in the doghouse as we debated the problem. Then as the ship lurched it suddenly wheeled and rolled six feet and smashed the wooden grill of the deck next to the shooting platform. There it wedged itself long enough for us to scurry around it with securing lines in hand and lash it in place like Lilliputians around Gulliver. The other scientists came out to help and we all surveyed the fantail as best we could, considering that the light on top of the doghouse was out. It quickly developed that the inboard sides of the cribs containing the seismic hydrophone cable were smashed. The top of one crib had disappeared over the side. Two of the cables were crushed and broken where the weightstand had brushed them. And somehow the pointed tip of one of the hydrophone floats had been driven through the side of the crib. It looked like one of those straws driven through a pane of window glass by a tornado. All electrical connections to the doghouse, which was the focus of the complicated communications for the seismic runs, had been broken by the weightstand. When Alan Jones flashed a light into the doghouse he found that the supplies and equipment drawers on one side had fallen out and spilled the contents on the floor. This puzzled him because they all had catches designed to keep them shut. Damage to the critical radio sets and recorders was not evident but without power he could not tell what had happened. The mystery of the drawers was solved as soon as he walked around the doghouse, avoiding waves that still occasionally curled over the guard railings. The outboard side of the doghouse had been caved in by the impact of one end of a heavy dredge which was still lashed in place at the other end. The drawer catches did not work because the whole wall was sprung. As a crowning misfortune, the wind had blown the radio antenna away, possibly when it was snapped by impact of the weightstand against the doghouse.

The windscreen and microphone attached to the shooting platform as well as the whole tilting table section were torn away. As we worked to unscramble the various hydrophone and magnetometer cables suspended over the side and

lashed and repaired fantail damage, I asked Alan Jones if he
could splice the broken cables and he showed me that he
could not unless they could be shielded from the salt spray—
which would require quiet waters. Contemplating the damage
it seemed clear that we could not be ready for the coming
seismic station without major repairs. After a conference to get
more of an estimate of what was involved, we set course for
Brisbane which was the nearest protected harbor. We tried to
raise *Horizon* on the radio to tell them of our plans and let
them meet us and obtain the fuel and water which they
thought necessary before going on to Auckland. So much for
our first effort to sample the elusive basement under the
pelagic blanket of the Lord Howe Rise.

About two weeks earlier Al Rowe, who keeps the air-gun
going come what may, and I had spent some time trying to
identify the parts of the system which might give us trouble
and need replacement. We had a basic air-gun plus a hodge-
podge of compressors, high-pressure hose connections, and
valves to put a shock into the water and a far more complex
streamer of hydrophones and electronics leading to two recorders. The parts had accumulated over a period of time and
without initial plan and it may be a little pompous to call the
aggregate a system. Nevertheless, it had a prime characteristic
of a system which was of vital importance to us as we sailed
around Melanesia collecting superb profiler records. Namely
it wouldn't work unless most of the parts worked. We had had
no previous history of continuous operation of the system at
high speeds and had no way of determining which parts would
fail most frequently and therefore needed many spares. When
I was in La Jolla I kept getting urgent messages to fly spare
parts out to the next port. Now I was on the ship and we were
sending urgent messages to La Jolla asking to have spare
parts flown to the next port. Shortly after leaving Noumea
two high-pressure hoses failed. After repairs, Al assembled a
list showing the working life before failure for pieces of the
three types of hose involved. They had lasted from as little as
ten hours to more than seven hundred and the failures appeared to be quite random. The same system on land presumably would last for decades, but not so on a moving and

vibrating ship. After viewing the very short inventory of hose parts and considering that unreplaced failure of any of the three sections would stop the operation, we suddenly realized we had a very serious problem. The expectable life of the system was something like a day and we were three weeks out of the next scheduled port.

We started to scour the ship for high-pressure hose but despite all the high-pressure gas storage tanks aboard we could find none. A radio call to *Horizon* indicated the same thing, although they had a spare small compressor which we could cannibalize for parts. That could give us a little more freedom of action because we could operate a less effective subsystem with our small compressor if the big one and its connecting hoses failed. We sent off additional urgent radio messages but I knew that if the main system failed we probably would have to stop at the nearest industrialized port where we might expect immediate replacement of parts. As we headed for Brisbane the main system failed. Six hours later the small subsystem overheated and we turned it off and suspended profiling. If we had not already been on our way to Brisbane, at that moment we would have started. At least we would not have to worry about a lack of high-pressure hose after we left Brisbane, of that we would make sure.

You may recall that our courtship with the port of Brisbane had become involved by our possession of explosives during the seismic work. Consequently *Horizon* had paid a call during Leg I of *Nova* when she carried no explosives, but on the present leg we had jilted the port for Noumea. After that decision was made it developed that our visit would have been acceptable if we had agreed to anchor out in the bay rather than proceed upriver to Brisbane proper. Thus we knew that we could enter the bay and effect our repairs and probably obtain launches to take us into the multitudinous delights of Brisbane. As we approached the continent, we moved farther from the center of the storm and the wind and swell abated. Three, then a dozen, then more porpoises appeared to play tag with our questing bow. The shallow sea grew greener and the bluffs of Moreton Island rose above the horizon to the southwest. A great Moreton Bay fig from this area is

visible from the dock at Point Loma where *Argo* has a home
berth. With binoculars we could also see Norfolk pines, which
are native only to Norfolk Island. They were to give us our
only contact with the island because we had had to abandon
our plans for a visit in order to make up the time we were losing in Brisbane. After a long passage down the bay we anchored, explosives and all, in a kind of quarantine off the
Brisbane River mouth and watched ships cleared by customs
go up and down to the city. Being confined to the ship for a
whole day we managed to effect many of the essential repairs
which had brought us into quiet waters. The work went on
well into the night and began again the next morning as we
again waited for some very pleasant officials to complete their
tedious business. By early afternoon we had done everything
necessary to justify a visit ashore, we were cleared and off we
went up the full river and past the refineries and into Brisbane.
I spent most of the day looking at paintings and almost bought
another Pro Hart showing a eucalyptus grove but I couldn't
quite make a decision. I stayed the night in the hotel which
was General MacArthur's headquarters during the Second
World War and tried to visualize his staff scurrying about. At
that time in the Solomon Islands the Marines had a little song:

> We asked for the Army to come to Tulagi,
> But General MacArthur said "No."
> He said "There's a reason.
> This isn't the season
> Besides there is no USO."

That was many years ago.

I met *Horizon* as she came to the fueling dock early the
next morning. Having only Nitramon she could enter the sacred
river but go only halfway to port. George Shor and my com-
panions of the previous month on *Horizon* had a lot to tell me
about their experiences and we looked at records and discussed plans. *Horizon*, in addition to needing fuel and water,
had just developed one of those mysterious malaises which
affect our ships when they touch land. Sometimes I think it is a
kind of hay fever brought on by the least speck of dry dust.
Suddenly she needed urgent and critical repairs and the prog-

nosis was that the illness would take at least a day to run its course. That is a minimum for this type of ship's illness so I was not surprised, although I had hoped that some immunity might have developed from two other attacks that *Horizon* suffered each time that we were in Suva during the last month.

The illness was not contagious. *Argo* finished all repairs and laden with kangaroo skins and memories of a friendly city sailed on schedule into a glassy calm. Down the continental slope we went, passing lightly over many a shallow submarine canyon. Across the Tasman abyssal plain stretching flat as a billiard table for a hundred miles until we came to one of the Tasmantid guyots which we had first crossed on our way west during the storm. It lies in a long north-south line of ancient volcanoes more or less in the center of the deep Tasman Basin. This one is a majestic peak 14,000 feet high, rising above the perfectly flat plain. It has only the designation "NT–1" on modern oceanographic charts but it appears to be part of the Britannia Hills discovered half a century ago. We called it Britannia Guyot. The top is at a depth of 1300 to 1400 feet and is somewhat irregular for a guyot. Dan Karig made the usual survey and once again we positioned ourselves for the dredging game. The first dredge bit firmly into the bottom and the half-inch steel plate was broken at the welds when we brought it back on deck. This was the third dredge that had so broken during *Nova* and it had never happened before in eighteen years so we knew we had had some indifferent welding when the dredge was made in La Jolla. Nevertheless the dredge had been subjected to very strong tension and the bottom was very hard. We had obtained another sample of phosphatized foram ooze but it seemed unlikely it had broken the dredge. We put another dredge on the line and maneuvered into position. On the bottom the dredge caught against outcrops and our tensiometer showed strains of 4000 pounds or slightly more in the cable. After an hour we hauled up the dredge and Fred Dixon kept pulling sideways on the cable as it came in. He was suspicious that we had lost the dredge and he was absolutely right. The end was bare. The elaborate strain gauge needed adjustment because the wire does not break at 4000 pounds tension; it is not even permanently stretched. We wanted a datable sample in the worst way in order to get a clue about the age and history of this whole chain of submarine volcanoes. Our first sample had by this time been identified as containing Pliocene fossils a few million years old, but they were pelagic types which had lived at the surface and merely fallen on the guyot sometimes after it became submerged. We wanted a reef coral or some other datable organism which had lived on the guyot when it was a very shallow bank. We put a third dredge on the cable and went through the whole procedure again. This time we retrieved the dredge and more of the phosphatized foram ooze and we had to give up in order to make our rendezvous with *Horizon* for the next seismic station. Even with good weather, adequate time, and successful dredging you can only sample what is on the bottom—not what you would like to have there to solve your problems.

The stop at Brisbane had had a valuable bonus in that we had obtained the plots, profiles, and other records from *Horizon* for analysis and comparison with our records on *Argo*. For the first time we could really study the banks and guyots described to us over the radio. The sum of our efforts was satisfactorily more significant than the parts. The integrated concept of the *Nova* Expedition was paying off. From Nova Guyot on the north to Gifford Guyot on the south extends a 300-mile-long, north-south line of six modern and ancient islands and we had now crossed every one, and surveyed and dredged three. The records in hand showed that all the flat guyot tops are at almost exactly the same depth of 900 feet. This may not sound very surprising but it is unique in the world, and means that the whole long line has subsided just the same amount. Many lines and groups of guyots are known but none that have sunk with such extraordinary regularity. The amount of vertical movement is not exceptional, nor is the geographical extent unusual. Very extensive marine terraces, for example, have been elevated hundreds to thousands of feet along the coasts of Canada and Scandinavia. These terraces were cut at sea level when Pleistocene glaciers loaded and depressed the continental crust of the Northern Hemisphere. When the glaciers melted and the load vanished, the continents and their shorelines rose. All this history can be reconstructed just from the differential movements and ages of the shorelines. Other differential vertical movements can likewise be explained by various geological processes such as sea floor spreading or expansion and contraction of the mantle. But the Nova-Gifford guyots present a different problem. What process is capable of producing extensive and very uniform sinking of 900 feet?

Let us marshal the evidence available on board *Argo* as it sailed across the Tasman Sea. The guyots are all at the same depth and they have sunk slowly because several form the broad platforms from which coral reefs have grown upward and now form drowned atolls. The guyots are truncated volcanoes and were once volcanic islands but now are covered with phosphatized foram ooze of uncertain age. That is all we know about the guyots themselves but it is a reasonable surmise that they are all of closely similar age because they lie along a single crack in the crust. What made them sink the same distance? Each forms a load on the crust but the weight must have been balanced by a thickening of the crust or other effect as the volcanoes grew upward. They could hardly have been sinking when rivers and waves truncated them to such level platforms. Consequently it appears that the whole region has somehow sunk. Vertical motion of the mantle or folding of the crust has not produced such regular sinking anywhere else and thus seems unlikely. Sea floor spreading seems even less probable because of the uniformity required. No, the sinking seems to be the result of some constant and gentle but persistent stress. Can it be the loading of the sea floor by the constant fall of tiny foram shells? Nothing could be gentler nor more uniform but is the expectable effect large enough to be important?

Our profiler records show a thick blanket of sediment around the guyots. We already have the data to answer the question. Our seismic refraction stations give us the velocity at which shock waves are propagated through the sediment. An empirical relationship established by Drs. Nafe and Drake at Lamont Geological Observatory enables us to convert velocity into density of the sediment. From all this we can calculate that the density of the sediment ranges from 1.9 grams/cc at the base to probably 1.45 grams/cc at the surface. If the average value is 1.62 grams/cc, the load of the pelagic blanket of horizontal sediment we see with our air-gun is just sufficient to depress the oceanic crust by 900 feet. Thus the gentle "snow-fall" of microscopic shells may very well have pushed the sea floor down into the mantle and forced a mighty chain of volcanic islands to sink beneath the waves. This is no more fantastic than that real snowflakes piled up so thickly in Scandinavia that the continent sank—and it did.

Having finished our dredging we sailed overnight to our rendezvous point for Seismic Station F. The sky was cloudless, and the weather pleasant. While waiting for *Horizon* we had attempted to measure heat flow but the probe once again did not penetrate far enough to give a valid result. *Horizon* arrived and streamed hydrophones and we departed to the southeast on our shooting run across the deep and level Tasman abyssal plain. This station would give us the crustal structure of the deep sea between Australia and the Lord Howe Rise and as we continued east we would make similar measurements on the rise itself. First, however, and as soon as Seismic Station F was finished, both ships would go straight to the western boundary cliffs of the rise, and sample the exposed basement which had been beyond our grasp before we were driven into Brisbane. George Shor and I spent some time on the radio coordinating our plans for this crucial sampling —wasted time as it developed.

The shooting run continued through the morning and the wind began to sing through the rigging and whip the tops of the waves into tiny whitecaps. *Horizon* reported an unsuccessful attempt to measure heat flow, but she would try again later in the day. We stopped and streamed hydrophones to listen and *Horizon* shot toward us. The wind was 25 knots and the swell was confused and rising. Streaming hydrophones was a cold and wet chore as the fantail dipped beneath the higher waves and ankle deep water sloshed the length of the deck. The sky went from clear blue to completely grey within a few hours and was clear again for a star sight when *Horizon* at last shot her way beside us. The wind was at 35 knots and the forecast was for continuing gales. The swell was too high for work and both ships had to suspend sampling. Once again the weather was slowly stripping us of our capabilities. It was about to speed up the process. Al Rowe had at last fabricated a complete new hydrophone streamer to act as a reserve for the air-gun system and he naturally was eager to test it. This involved a lengthy period of hauling in on one line and paying out on another as we all got cold and wet on the fantail. The result was joking with the soaking as usual, and everyone was in high good humor as we moved back into the shelter of the laboratory and removed boots or dried bare feet according to individual practice. We turned on the air-gun and collected round to watch the recorder indicate the quality of the new hydrophone system. No record, what was wrong? Nothing in the laboratory electronics, so we slowed the ship and went out into the wet to haul in and check the streamer. We did not have to haul far because beyond the end of the electrical cable there was no streamer. The new fittings had not stood the test of dragging through stormy waters and we would not have a proper reserve air-gun streamer in case anything happened. Things do happen. Not an hour after we had once again put out the old faithful streamer, George Shor came on the radio to record further disasters. After getting under way, *Horizon* was moving along slowly to pay out the magnetometer and the cables and streamers for the arcer—the electrical equivalent of our air-gun. One of the large waves had driven the ship back over the arcer hydrophones and the streamer had been lost. Could we provide another? I gave him the sad news that he was an hour too late. We did, however, have an older type of short streamer in the hold and he could have that when next it was calm enough for a transfer. That would be better than the even older type he had in reserve. You may recall that this profiling equipment was constantly changing and consequently we often still had parts with varying degrees of obsolescence aboard. What George had remaining permitted him to profile at 6 knots, which was as fast as Tom Chase and Stu Smith had been able to do during the reconnaissance phase of *Nova* only four months before. After we transferred the intermediate quality streamer he would be able to speed up a bit more. This difference in speeds was going to make planning joint operations more complicated because *Argo* could now profile faster than *Horizon* could cruise and almost twice as fast as she could profile. Instead of a task force we would be more like a one-ship convoy with a one-ship circling escort, or like a small planet with a big satellite.

The time to face reality was again at hand. We simply could not execute our plans to dredge and core the basement outcrops on the western cliffs and we had no time to wait until the weather improved. So much for planning, so much for reconnaissance, so much for scheduling, so much for perserverance, so much for the western cliffs and the outcrops of the basement. We would have to improvise and somehow find outcrops in the unpromising part of the rise to the east.

The next day we had another seismic station, measured heat flow, and enjoyed ever-improving weather. Then we sailed east again toward a big shoot on the crest of the rise. Because our speeds were so different, *Horizon* went on a straight line between stations and we went on a long zigzag. We thought that we might be able to detect some old river valleys under the pelagic blanket. By this time the *Nova* Expedition had collected numerous profiles of the basement topography of the Lord Howe Rise, but the logistics of exploration had caused almost all of them to be perpendicular to the rise and therefore we were not likely to find any valleys, which probably would also be perpendicular to it. Yet such valleys existed at one time if the rise was ever part of the continent of Tasmantis. Continents are eroded by rivers in valleys. By running parallel to the rise we tried to find such valleys but were not successful. Perhaps we did not look far enough, but perhaps the basement we could see with the air-gun had had a peculiar history and had been eroded by waves just below sea level. How helpful a sample of the basement would have been to limit speculation.

Basement was below us but under a pelagic blanket 1500 feet thick. We stopped for a seismic station and *Horizon* came with a bent bow and emptying of magazines on the start of what we expected would be a very long shoot because of the thick crust. While we listened we also tried to sample the bottom with a piston core which is capable of sampling thirty feet deep. But not this time—all we recovered for our effort was a few hundred tiny foram shells in a very white ooze—just a bit of fluff from the pelagic blanket. If we could not sample, we could always look, and Fred Dixon lowered his deep sea camera again. We had an idea that a broad pass cutting across the crest of the rise might be the result of current scour or might provide a channel for currents. Such currents produce visible evidence of their existence in the form of scours or ripple marks or other disturbances of the sediment surface like those found on sandy beaches or river beds. When Fred emerged from the darkroom we could view the sea floor 4900 feet below, and a nondescript sight it was. The camera had immortalized a fish, and a few other organisms and a mottled and pockmarked bottom. Not the kind of pictures we were hoping for. Still, the position and depth, even the existence of the broad pass were uncertain, based as they were on older soundings of unknown reliability. Perhaps the pass was still ahead of us, in fact where *Horizon* was now sailing on the shooting run. "Yes," they said by radio, "the bottom does dip downward in a pass east of your present position." We could look farther along for evidence of scour by currents.

*Horizon* stopped almost ninety miles away and we began our last long run across the Lord Howe Rise in the very early hours of the morning. The pelagic blanket beneath us was roughly 2000 feet thick. I awoke to the distant and muffled gun of Nitramon exploding in the water behind the ship. On deck the sea and sky looked like an advertisement for a south sea cruise—warm, clear, calm, and with the faintest wind ripples moving in cat's paws across a glassy sea. Now this was a day when anything could happen. I walked down to the laboratory and found the watchstander staring at the air-gun recorder as if it were a crystal ball and he could see his own future. The pelagic blanket was only 1000 feet thick and with every five-second sweep of the recorder it was getting thinner. We were in the broad pass reported by *Horizon* and we were suddenly filled with optimism that currents might have prevented deposition of the blanket and that exposed outcrops of basement might lie ahead. *Horizon* would not have found them because we do not think it safe to run the arcer and drop explosives so she does not profile on seismic shooting runs. For an hour we watched each sweep and at 0706 hours on 30 August the blanket was gone and the basement lay bare below us ready for sampling. A few minutes later it dipped again beneath the blanket for we had to continue on the shooting run. However, the blanket was thin for most of an hour and we knew we could return because *Horizon* and the end of the run were only thirty miles ahead. The blanket was about 400 feet thick when the ships were side by side and we agreed that *Horizon* should proceed east seeking outcrops to sample while we went back to look for the one we had found or even a bigger one.

The atmosphere on the ship was joyful and expectant as we began our search. Our noon position introduced our first worry. We appeared to have drifted several miles since our previous star fix and we were now setting out to find an outcrop less than a mile across. From dead reckoning navigation alone this obviously was impossible, although we might be lucky. Our hopes, so firmly founded it seemed, now rested on two possibilities: "our" outcrop might be one of many in the area of thin blanket, or by improvising a new survey technique we might home in on an outcrop. We turned somewhat northwest of our previous track because the older soundings indicated a broad peak and we thought it might be an outcrop swept free by currents. Simultaneously we started a new type of plot, or at least new to us. We plotted depths along the assumed ship track in pencil, as usual, and thickness of the blanket in red. We added the blanket thickness in notes along the sounding track of the shooting run. Now, instead of just depth, we could use sediment thickness to check our navigation as well as find an outcrop.

At first most of the scientists were glued to the air-gun recorder or "geovision," as we began to call it. After a few hours, however, the tension gradually depleted the ranks of the faithful. The survey continued and when the blanket thickened to the northwest we turned south toward our first, and only, outcrop. The south sea cruise atmosphere continued and people were sunning, reading, talking, and exercising about the deck. Periodically, however, the lure of the geovision would be too much and back they would come to see what was happening. The blanket was only 120 feet by midafternoon when we began to follow an expanding spiral search pattern. Without satellite navigation there was nothing more that we could do to put us back on our outcrop. Well, there was something we could do. Duffy McGowan decided a cup of cocoa would have to be acceptable as a libation to luck since she was on watch, and she offered it. The basement did not immediately respond; we were tantalized as it moved up and down while the top of the sediment remained relatively level. Sometimes the blanket was a little thicker and sometimes a little thinner until at last, at long last, it was threadbare and as Lee Bell chanted "Yeah, basement go," it emerged when we had perfect weather and could stop. We did.

The sport of harrying and chivying sub-bottom reflectors until they emerge and can be sampled was developed in the Atlantic by Maurice Ewing and colleagues at Lamont Geological Institute. For sampling they always considered the piston corer as the appropriate weapon in the oceanographic armory. Accordingly we had rigged our piston corer ready to lower away as soon as we stopped and before we drifted off the hard-won outcrop. Down it went in 4500 feet of water. Up it came, empty. We rerigged, and down it went again. Up it came. We must have been nervous because it had not triggered—we had started to haul up before it reached the bottom. Down it went again without even bringing it aboard. Up again, and behold, our priceless sample was flowing like milk out of the bottom of the coring tube. We caught it in buckets and sieves but found a little solid sample remaining in the corer when it was at last safely on deck. We had in hand some of the basement for which we had fought so long, a few small pebbles of consolidated sediment.

But for consolidated sediment the appropriate weapon is the dredge rather than the piston corer. Once more dear friends and it was over the side. The strain gauge indicated a pull of 3000 pounds as it dragged through the bottom. Then the gauge went rapidly to 3750 pounds and decreased soon after. We should have had a good sample of the basement. Up it came; we peered over the fantail into the water; looked into the dredge as it broke water; the bottom was full of rock; on deck, it was inverted and tumbled out; quickly it went into a box and safely into the laboratory.

A few days later I noticed a quotation in the introduction to the narrative of the *Challenger* Expedition which seemed entirely appropriate to that moment. It originally appeared in a publication in 1862 and refers to a sample obtained in the North Atlantic at a depth of 7560 feet. "That single sounding," says Dr. Wallich, "I may be permitted to say compensated for every disappointment that weather and accident may have previously engendered. At the eleventh hour, and under circumstances the most unfavourable for searching out its secrets, the deep has sent forth the long-coveted message."

We had an ancient foram ooze, hardened by long exposure at the sea floor, partially replaced by phosphorite and manganese oxides, broken into fragments, and undermined and riddled through with tunnels made by worms. It was the time of the micropaleontologist who can identify the individual species of foram present and, since the species live for only short geological periods, can tell the age of the rock. We had on board all the necessary ingredients: a microscope, sampling equipment, publications describing and figuring the forams of different ages in Melanesia, and Warren Smith. You might think that fossils are dry as dust and paleontologists have eternity for their work. However, the literature on board was as timely as the lastest model of hydrophone streamer for the arcer. We had a reprint of "Late Tertiary Biostratigraphy (Planktonic Foraminifera) of Tropical Indo-Pacific Deep-Sea Cores," by my colleague Franny Parker, which she published in June 1967 just after Ned Allison and I left La Jolla. Ned's wife obtained a copy of the paper and airmailed it to Noumea in time for it to go to sea on *Argo* and here it was at just the right place to identify the basement age of the Lord Howe Rise. The tiny forams have astonishing names and these were no exception. Warren showed us his slides and identified *Sphaeroidinella subdehiscens*, *Sphaeroidinella seminulina*, and some doubtful *Globorotalia acostaensis*, and that was that. The fossil ooze was of middle to upper Miocene age.

By the standard isotopic time scale such an age was

about 15 million years ago and that enables us to tie together various events. "Basement" covers material of various ages and it would be misleading to attach this age to everything just below the pelagic blanket. However, lacking other information, let us assume that the erosion surface we have called the basement has this age. Then prior to 15 million years ago the core of the Lord Howe Rise (Melantis?) was buried under thousands of feet of sedimentary rock which was folded and faulted and eroded to an approximate plain. At least the top and perhaps all of this sedimentary rock was foraminiferal ooze such as collects on banks and deeper submarine shoals. This rock was swept off the center of the rise and deposited around the flanks as we can see from the thickening of the layers in the air-gun records. Thus the rise grew broader and flatter as time passed. For some reason deposition stopped for a time 15 million years ago and was not renewed until the beginning of deposition of the undisturbed pelagic blanket at an unknown later time. The blanket is as much as 3300 feet thick and averages roughly half that. If deposition began not long after 15 million years ago, the rates of sedimentation have ranged from one to two inches per millennium, which is quite reasonable considering known rates of deposition in other shallow warm seas.

In all these banks and shoals being eroded near sea level do we see Melantis? To answer this question we have to consider the deeper structure revealed by geophysical techniques during *Nova*.

---

---

# *Why Shallow?*

**CHAPTER ELEVEN** We have crossed again the New Caledonia Trough and the great Norfolk Ridge, making a seismic station on each. Now as we sail the nameless waters between the ridge and the Kermadec Islands it seems a good time to take stock of what we have been doing and consider whether we have answered any of the questions we set out to study. I do not mean to suggest that further analysis of the data will not reveal much more than we know now. Of course it will. New and undetected problems and perhaps even answers are hidden in our data. Nevertheless there is a timeliness about this particular time. We have just done the work and can remember everything affecting the quality of the measurements. Helen and I discussing the first crustal section we measured on the Lord Howe Rise a few weeks ago both instantly recall that the crustal thickness is doubtful because the timing circuit broke down on the last shot. Likewise, if not now, when will the results be considered? We shall know nothing more in November than we do now in early September because most of the samples and detailed records will be in the magazine of *Horizon* sailing home. It will then take several months of sorting, cataloging, and filing before we are in a position to advance our knowledge beyond what we know now. We should be able to confirm certain tentative conclusions in time to present them at the April meeting of the American Geophysical

Union in Washington, D.C. A few short notes about the results may be published by next summer but they will contain little not now known. More complete results with elaborate and comprehensive illustrations and tables should be submitted for publication in scientific journals about a year from now by a few of the most fortunate and industrious investigators, and at increasingly remote times by others. Thus while it is not a choice of now or never, it is one of the same world being with us late and soon.

Consequently we accelerate the data analysis which has being going on continuously. Helen calculates the crustal sections and Jean graphs them; Colin and Graham plot the thickness of the pelagic blanket along the ship tracks produced by Dan and others. Warren looks at his foram slides, Fred develops pictures, Sean plots magnetic profiles; and everyone helps and stands watches and carries out other special chores. One of the great advantages of data analysis at sea is that nothing interferes except the acquisition of more data. That is one reason why we shall know nothing more than we do now for many months to come. Seven 12-hour days produce much more than five 8-hour days and they do not cost the university any more. Put in other terms, however, the scientists could have earned as much and spent far less government money by staying at home and surfing at noon and on weekends. What has been gained by the *Nova* Expedition? I have tried to indicate some of the results and their significance as we acquired them. I shall deal with others shortly. Now I want to consider what we have learned bearing on a very simple question, why is Melanesia so shallow?

When the expedition was planned several possible explanations for the extraordinarily shallow water were available: a continent, Melantis, once existed in the area and had broken up and somehow become thinner and sunk; a normal ocean basin crust had been elevated in a Melanesian Rise by the same mantle convection which elevates midocean ridges; a continent was in the process of development by accumulation of molten rock derived from the interior of the earth but had not reached normal thickness and thus was still under water. Our results, mainly from the seismic stations and profiler records, show that more than one cause has had an important effect but that one of the most significant was not predicted. Instead of dynamic and dramatic events, surprising effects have come from the silent, invisible, painfully slow but enduring fall of pelagic snow.

Let us consider a normal ocean depth and crustal structure for comparison with those found in Melanesia. The open ocean basins are about three miles deep and below is a crust consisting of a thousand feet of mud and ooze, about half a mile of sedimentary rock and cooled lava flows, and three miles of "oceanic layer," which is the one which propagates seismic waves with high velocity. For comparison with our new measurements it is convenient to see how deep the water would be if the mud and sedimentary rock layers were removed but not the oceanic layer. Two effects would occur if we dredged these layers away from any large region, for example one the size of Southern California. First, water would rush in and fill the hole so the water depth would increase another 4300 feet. Second, the crust would begin to rise and the mantle would flow into the hole under the crust and the water depth would decrease to only about 1500 feet more than it was originally. At that depth the weight of the additional water above the oceanic layer and the additional mantle below the oceanic layer would be just equal to the weight of the mud and sedimentary rock dredged away. This balancing is called "isostasy," which merely means "equal weight" in Greek. It may seem unlikely that the rock of the mantle flows like water to affect a balance, but no geological fact is better documented. Lake Mead is a tiny artificial lake formed by the construction of Boulder Dam. Careful releveling and resurveying of the surrounding desert has proved that the new load of the lake water has bowed the crust downward and this means that the mantle has flowed outward from under the lake.

So we can calculate the depth of water if we mentally remove any layer of the sea bottom. Let us play the numbers game with the water depth and crustal section at the seismic station on the abyssal plain between New Caledonia and the Loyalty Islands. At one end of the station the water depth is

3900 feet and at the other it is 4100 feet. Likewise the layers below have slightly different thicknesses. Taking average values the mud and ooze are 2800 feet thick and the harder and denser layer below is 2200 feet thick. The underlying oceanic layer averages 4.8 miles thick, which is greater than normal for ocean basins but not much. The depth is most peculiar and might be explained by a remarkable crust or violent motions of the mantle. Take but the sediment away, however, and after adjustment the water depth becomes 2.7 miles, which is well within the range of normal oceanic depths. The possibility of a peculiar crust is eliminated by the observations, and the necessity for violent mantle motion, at present, is obviated by the alternative mechanism of sedimentation and isostasy. Occam's razor says that the simplest explanation should be accepted as the correct one.

What of the other parts of Melanesia? I cannot yet say much about the areas studied by Helsley and Winterer except that the sediment in the Gulf of Papua is thick and the bottom is shallow. Shor's work gives a widespread correlation between shallow depth and thick sediment. It was obvious enough at the time from the air-gun records that the pelagic blanket in Melanesia is far thicker in most places than it is in the deep central oceans. What is surprising in the seismic data is that the mud and ooze layer is generally two or three times thicker than the pelagic blanket. A happy exception is the second station on the Lord Howe Rise, where we found and sampled an outcrop of the basement. There, the pelagic blanket indicated by the air-gun is the same as for the seismic technique. Nevertheless in most places the folded, faulted and eroded "basement" of the air-gun is only an intermediate layer in sediment commonly 6000 to 7000 feet thick. Below is the harder and denser layer 6000 to 13,000 feet thick and consisting of sedimentary rock with perhaps some old lava flows. These thicknesses are very widespread, essentially everywhere that we found a thick pelagic blanket. What is the effect of this sediment on the water depth? The depth of the South Fiji Basin averages 2.7 miles but, sans sediment, it is 3.4 miles or the same as the open ocean basins. The New Caledonia Basin west of the island is far shallower—only 2.3 miles—but with the sediment removed it too would be a normal oceanic depth, even a little deep, at 3.6 miles. Both these stations, like the Loyalty trough, have normal oceanic layers and thus their depth can be completely explained by supposing that they were once normal deep oceanic crust which has been covered with thick sediment. The Tasman Basin and the west flank of the Lord Howe Rise have an oceanic layer with a wave propagation velocity that is slightly slow, but the thickness is average and it does not strain the definition much to call them both normal. The depth of the basin is 3.0 miles, or the same as a standard deep ocean location, and the west flank of the rise is only 2.1 miles deep. However, if the thick sediment at each of these localities were removed the water depth would be a spectacular 3.9 miles in the basin and 3.3 miles under the flank of the rise. Thus the western side of the rise would be as deep as normal sea floor and the basin would be considerably deeper.

What is the nature of this sediment? It appears to have more than one source. In the Tasman Basin and part of the New Caledonia Basin and in local pockets the sediment has been deposited by bottom currents moving from adjacent land or undersea mountains. In the South Fiji Basin, for example, we cored a mud containing pebbles of an older, harder mud which had to be transported for a short distance along the bottom. For another type of evidence, the undersea margin of Australia is cut by numerous canyons down which, presumably, mud and sand flow to the Tasman abyssal plain. The other major source of sediment is the snowfall of microscopic shells which produces the pelagic blanket draping most of Melanesia. In addition various other things fall into the water such as ash from volcanic eruptions, dust from faraway deserts, and cosmic dust from even more remote outer space. The aggregate thickness from all these exotic sources is trivial, and it seems that most of the upper sediment blanketing Melanesia is pelagic ooze.

Is the lower sediment a limestone produced by the usual processes that convert oozes to hard rock? We have no way of telling, although it might be possible with more searching and dredging. From our successful quest on the Lord Howe

Rise we know that the top of the basement under the upper blanket is phosphatized and hardened foram ooze. Moreover the seismic velocities in the basement are what might be expected for a limestone. Other lines of evidence are more tenuous; for example, we observed that the pelagic blanket on the Lord Howe Rise tends to reduce underlying relief by differentially filling troughs. We also saw that this same phenomenon occurs as deep as we could look into the basement, and this suggests that the basement may be a deeper equivalent of the surface blanket.

Granted that most of this region is unusually shallow because it is covered with unusually thick pelagic ooze, we can turn to the question of why the ooze is so thick. First, however, we should consider the shallow regions of Melanesia which cannot be completely explained by thick oozes. As it will develop, the accretion of oozes may be related to the origin of these shallow regions. The Fiji Plateau is very shallow but lacks much of a mud or ooze cover. The Norfolk Ridge and Lord Howe Rise have nonoceanic crusts. At least two more explanations are necessary to explain why these regions are shallow. First let us consider the Fiji Plateau. It is shallow and has high heat flow. Mud and ooze are thin or absent but underlying sedimentary rock and lavas are 3000 to 10,000 feet thick. The oceanic layer is normal in most places but a little thick just south of the Fiji Islands. The water depth at Seismic Station M, only 1.7 miles, is close to average for the plateau. Without the ooze and underlying sedimentary and lava layer, the depth would still be only 2.2 miles. The remaining oceanic layer is about as thick as usual and consequently a great mountain of mantle is holding up the plateau. The extraordinary heat flow presumably is related to this upward bulge of the mantle, but I prefer to withhold further discussion until we deal with related matters in the next chapter, on movements of the crust in Melanesia. Suffice for the moment that the shallow depth of the Fiji Plateau requires an upward push under the crust rather than a snowfall on top of it.

The great ridge and rise of Melanesia seem to be shallow for quite another reason, namely they have a thick crust and may, in fact, be relics of Melantis. The crust of the Norfolk

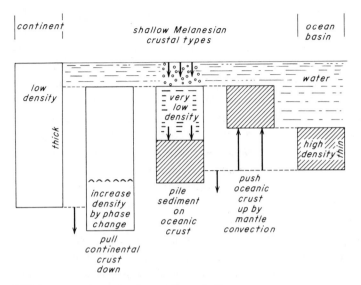

**Different ways to make the sea floor shallow.**

Ridge was not fully penetrated because we had not world enough nor time on our seismic station. Nevertheless we know it has a crust with a complex sequence of unusually thick layers. It is not at all like a normal oceanic crust and it is hardly surprising that just beyond the end of our seismic station lies the continental, if peculiar, island of New Caledonia, nor that at the other end of the great ridge is the northern peninsula of New Zealand. Whether this thin strip of not-quite-continental crust is growing more or less continental is obscure. If it was formerly part of broad Melantis we might expect some evidence of former erosion at sea level and this we did not find. On the contrary, at one locality was a blanket of pelagic ooze which was building the ridge upward and which might reach levels where coral could become attached and build further to sea level. The Norfolk Ridge remains enigmatic.

The Lord Howe Rise was less secretive than the great ridge, although perhaps only because we devoted much more time to it. Shor had obtained a complete and duplicated crustal structure on our southern line and an unduplicated and

more questionable structure in the beastly weather to the
north. Without doubt the rise is underlain by a semicontinental
crust, thick and with some layers with nonoceanic velocities
and densities. At the two ends of the southern station the section differs somewhat but I shall give only average values. The
ooze of the pelagic blanket of course is thin and even absent
in a few places. The phosphatized and otherwise lithified ooze
of the layer below is about 2000 feet thick or only a fraction
of its value in most of Melanesia. The water depth of less than
a mile has not been decreased by the thickening of a pelagic
blanket. Below the obvious sediments and sedimentary rocks
is a layer about six miles thick which has a wave propagation
velocity commonly found in the granitic and metamorphic
rocks of continents but not in normal ocean basin crust. Deeper
still is the lowest layer of the crust, about eight miles thick
and with the velocity common to both ocean basins and the
lower part of the continental crust. The whole crust is as thick
as that of Japan or New Zealand and it seems that the puzzle
of the rise is not whether it once was part of the continent of
Melantis but why it is not now. The eroded sedimentary rocks
shown on the air-gun records suggest that the rise was once
at sea level, where such erosion normally occurs. However, as
I have indicated, we found that erosion and redeposition are
occurring now on the rise at depths of almost a mile. We have
more conclusive evidence of sinking in the uniform depth of
900 feet to which the platforms of the Nova-Gifford guyots have
subsided. The guyots are firmly anchored to the rise so they
have sunk together. However, as I have noted, the guyots
probably are sinking because of the increasing weight of the
thickening pelagic blanket. While the guyots sink the blanket
makes the rise shallower and if present conditions continue the
rise should grow up to sea level in the same manner as the
Norfolk Ridge. A few broad passages maintained by ocean
currents will interrupt the endless expanse of reefs. Does such
a place exist in the world? Indeed so; the Chesterfield Islands
and adjacent waters appear to be just exactly what the northern part of the rise will be. Perhaps, now that the suggested
deep trough separating the rise and the islands has been
proved spurious, the Chesterfields may be sensibly considered

as part of the rise in an advanced stage of development. In more southerly, and therefore colder, latitudes coral will not form reefs and thus northwest of New Zealand the rise will not reach sea level by this mechanism.

When the expedition was conceived we had a general idea that we would be able to discover why Melanesia is so shallow. We did not know which of the proposed causes was correct but a general optimism prevailed that the answer would be simple. Thus the observations collected on heat flow on the Fiji Plateau might be expected to be pertinent to why the Lord Howe Rise is shallow, and the crustal structures of the shallow areas might have much in common that would help us understand their origin. Instead, we have found various causes for shallow depths. If for analogy we equate the crust of the earth floating on the mantle with an ice floe floating in a lake, we find the surface high because: (1) the floe is covered with a blanket of feathers, or (2) it is exceptionally thick, or (3) an underwater spring is pushing it upward. Equivalents of all these phenomena occur in Melanesia. It appears that the heat flow in the Fiji Plateau region has nothing to do with the shallowness of the Lord Howe Rise. This leaves us with many more loose ends than we expected—and we expected a lot. If we had expended the whole of the *Nova* Expedition on the Fiji Plateau we might be able to say not only that the region is shallow because it is pushed up by a bulge in the mantle, but why the bulge exists. With our unexpectedly unrelated observations, we have little chance of extracting such information from the data. Well, *Nova* won't be the last oceanographic expedition, and it is puzzles that keep scientists at sea.

3 september-11 september 1967
CHAPTER TWELVE

# Sea Floor Spreading

**CHAPTER TWELVE**  By 3 September we had finished a seismic station at the eastern base of the Norfolk Ridge and were dredging and surveying independently again for four days, although much of that time would go to running east to the next rendezvous. Our previous effort in this line had been east of Australia when we allotted five days to dredging guyots and surveying the Lord Howe Rise. That was halted by storms and we had to put into Brisbane for repairs. Now we parted again from *Horizon* but in calm weather which we hoped would persist. Due to her irreplaceable loss of a high-speed hydrophone streamer, *Horizon* was still reduced to 8 or 9 knots, whereas we found that in good weather we could do almost 13. We balanced the time to rendezvous by sending her on a straight line to minimize running but with many planned sampling stops to use all her capabilities. Meanwhile we started off on a great sweeping survey without any expectation of stopping.

We were on the track of yet one more fracture zone. So far, we had been batting about 0.500 on *Nova*. The large fracture zone originally expected south of New Caledonia and extending west to Australia had turned into a rumble of erroneous old soundings. On the north side of New Caledonia our luck had been better. No fracture zone had been suspected when the expedition was planned or put to sea but new soundings gave an indication that could be tested by July. The basin north of New Caledonia and west of the New Hebrides looks very like Africa in shape and orientation. The fracture zone is in the position of the coast stretching from Nigeria to Liberia and parallel to and just north of the equator. Interestingly enough, another Africa-shaped basin exists in Melanesia—the South Fiji Basin. Does it have a fracture zone along the equivalent of its Ivory Coast? We discussed the possibility in the early summer but the information was even vaguer than north of New Caledonia. At sea we sketched the various logical possibilities of how such basins could be formed and what tests might be applied to differentiate them. Then came the electrifying news by radio from Jerry Winterer. In a few days of sounding he had taken a few glimmerings and turned them into the d'Entrecasteau fracture zone extending as a major feature across the floor of the Coral Sea. From that moment we were eager to try to find the equivalent fracture zone in the South Fiji Basin and had carefully reserved expedition time for the purpose. We were about to spend that reserve.

We were confronted with a problem in logistics. If the water had been removed and we had remained suspended in position like a balloon we would have seen an interesting land ahead of us to the east. We were over the border ranges and foothills of the great Norfolk Ridge and to the northeast were the same indefinite and little-known peaks we had crossed before. To the southeast, however, the mountains were more orderly with a generally north-south trend. Separating the two mountainous regions and trending more or less transversely would have been a third range, and it was the one of interest because fracture zones tend to trend transverse to other structures. Beyond all the mountains was the great plain of the South Fiji Basin where we would shoot the next seismic station. How should we seek the fracture zone? If we had been on the plain and surveying west, we could have gone to the transverse ranges and looked for a narrow trough or a great cliff and followed it. Unfortunately, we were on the vague western approach to the transverse ranges and we had to make a series of large zigzags centered on the supposed extension of the hypothetical fracture zone. We lacked information necessary to do more than lay out a track and ask the ship navigators to follow it and see what happened. In short, we had to make a preliminary reconnaissance in order to attempt a survey. We went into the search pattern and the watch standers collected results.

By dawn of the first full day the weather had changed to stormy with squalls on the horizon. I had to time my walking around the deck to avoid occasional pelting rain. All day we followed our pattern with only minor variations to take into account some of the trends and deeps we were finding. The wind gradually increased to 30 knots and the sea was splashed with foam. *Horizon* was in the same weather to the south. Were we going to be hounded by storms once again? All day we cast about seeking spoor, but rather than finding new and steep mountains we seemed to be leveling them. Two of the large troughs we set out to survey proved to be chimerical. Instead of deep irregular basins we found broad flat-floored valleys, like the great valley of California except for an occasional hill rising above the plains.

In the early evening we were over a bit of sloping plain when we observed a curious profile on the air-gun record. The top of the basement dropped abruptly and the thickness of the mud and ooze under the plain increased to almost 2000 feet and then, as we moved along, decreased again to nothing and a rocky hill appeared. At the time, our developing map gave no indication that this sediment-filled trough connected with anything else. So difficult is it to reorient thinking that it was fully five days later before anyone recognized that there we would have found the fracture zone if we had only been able to penetrate its unusual disguise.

We continued the pattern of surveying and went to bed without a hint that the morrow would bring anything more than stormy weather. We woke to 35-knot winds, gale warnings, and decks too wet for walking because of the spray from waves breaking over the bow. But in the laboratory was another story; we had crossed a narrow trough, 2200 feet deep, just where it was expected on the northern edge of the transverse ranges. However, a trough does not a triumph make and this was not even much of a trough as fracture zones go.

Breakfast was cheery and we went back to watch the echo sounder and the geovision on the air-gun recorder. The bottom on the north side of the trough continued shallow and after an hour we realized that we might be lured into a trap. The nearest sounding plotted on our charts was fifty miles ahead and, although it was in the deep floor of the basin, we had no way of knowing how far north the foothills of the transverse ranges extended. At some point soon we had to suppress the urge to look over the next mountain and get back to the fracture zone that we might already have found. By doing so we would give up the possibility of finding a bigger fracture zone at the boundary between the ranges and the deep floor of the basin, so we went for one more hour away from our trough before turning southeast into the weather.

We had some trouble with the air-gun and made a few course changes to provide protection while hauling and streaming cables, but everything was operational when we returned to the expected location of our trough. That was fortunate because the echo sounder showed no trough but rather a great cliff 3600 feet high. The air-gun supplied the trough; it was filled with sediment but clearly visible in the sub-bottom profile and a little more than 1200 feet deep. Our fracture zone began to look far more probable but also more difficult to follow than we had anticipated.

We continued into the heart of the transverse ranges to get some inkling of their nature. Where we went they were relatively flat on top because of a covering of pelagic blanket about 1000 feet thick. About this time we talked by radio with *Horizon* and George Shor told us they had found and dredged a guyot on the large mountain range which extended almost due south from the transverse ranges to the Three Kings Islands just off New Zealand. It was about 1200 feet deep and they had obtained reef corals giving clear proof of sinking by a similar amount. We left the high mountains, almost 11,000 feet above the South Fiji Basin abyssal plain, and again headed toward the trough or cliff or any other evidence of the fracture zone. Right on a line with the previous crossings came a narrow trough 2700 feet deep with sediment at least 300 feet deep in the bottom. We had a genuine fracture zone which had gouged a straight trough for at least fifty miles across the sea floor and which was in the predicted position to match the d'Entrecasteau fracture zone in the Coral Sea Basin. This was very interesting indeed, but was it a really major feature and if so, how far did it go and why and how did it stop and how old was it and . . . ? All we could do was to continue to look.

Another crossing and we found the same trough but with more filling of sediment. The day was gone but the survey went on. To bed at midnight and up at 3 to look at the new crossing. The trough had the same depth but was getting broader and the fill of sediment was much deeper. Changed course at 4 and back to sleep. Up before 7 to see the next crossing on the records carefully maintained by the watch. Now the trough was cutting across a spur of the higher mountains and it was more than half-filled by 1300 feet of sediment. We should be helpless without the air-gun in trying to trace this fracture zone. Two more crossings followed in rapid succession because by that time we were confident about the location of the fracture and because we no longer had so much time before our rendezvous. The trough persisted but it was at least half full of sediment. We turned northeast and the airgun hydrophone streamer parted a wire and stopped recording, and what could we do next? We could not stop because Shor's time would be wasted. He was far out in the abyssal plain and had found from repeated tries that he could not penetrate the bottom either more or less than three feet. Consequently, he could not do anything useful at all except steam toward the rendezvous. We could sound and tow the magnetometer so we continued on. At the expected continuation of the fracture zone we went over a low cliff and onto an abyssal plain. Was the trough under it? It always seems that the unobtainable is eminently desirable. Here the last crossing would have shown whether the trough continues under the abyssal plain and beyond the boundaries of the transverse ranges. We shall not know until Craig perhaps passes here in a month's time. Four hours later the air-gun was fully operational but then it was too late to help.

I suppose it is time to name the new fracture zone, which presents the usual problems. Some people, such as Winterer,

are blessed with finding fracture zones which are near something which suggests a handy name. I rarely find one anywhere near any land. The "South Fiji Basin fracture zone,"
the only geographical possibility, seems hopeless as a name.
The name of the ship or the expedition would be reasonable,
and some zones have been named after eminent earth scientists. Given the d'Entrecasteau zone to the north and the
Vening-Meinesz zone to the south, a name in honor of a great
Englishman and one of the first European explorers of these
waters seems entirely appropriate. We have then the "Cook
fracture zone."

What of the age of these two fracture zones discovered
during *Nova*? They seem more ancient than active. Neither is
the locus of earthquakes. A deeply subsided and therefore old
guyot is associated with the d'Entrecasteau fracture zone. The
main trough of the Cook fracture zone we have just found is
partially filled in most places with mud and ooze and thus has
existed for some time. Moreover, the sediment is undisturbed
except for a gentle sagging probably produced by compac-
tion under its own weight. The age of the sediment is unknown, but applying a fast rate of sedimentation of one inch in
a thousand years would give a minimum period of more than
10 million years since any activity in some places.

What is the significance of the fracture zones? Essentially,
they give us some critical information to help solve the puzzle
of whether the continents have drifted and the sea floor has
spread in Melanesia. They indicate the existence and even
suggest the direction of such motions of the crust in response
to convective motion in the mantle. The response, you will recall, takes two forms. The continental crust splits if convection
originates below it. This seems to be occurring now in the Red
Sea and the Gulf of California. If splitting continues or if convection originates to one side of a continent, the continent
drifts across the face of the globe. The gap created by splitting
continents is filled by spreading oceanic crust. The spreading
has been elegantly demonstrated by the discovery of symmetrical magnetic stripes in the rocks of the sea floor. For this
reason, with the hope of making similar demonstrations, we
have gone to great trouble to keep operational magnetometers

on our ships during *Nova*. Technically, this has been successful. All those radio and cable messages, that flight of a technician to Kwajalein, the frustrating air freight shipment to Suva, and Shawn Biehler's provision for a magnetometer from M.I.T. have resulted in continuous and reliable records on each ship for the last two months. But to what avail when we cannot find any magnetic stripes? We did detect the nonmagnetic mountains west of Fiji and we suspect north-trending stripes under the Fiji Plateau but they are questionable. A central problem is that our early breakdowns of magnetometers on the very long reconnaissance profiles left us with inadequate background information. The sounding and profiler records from the reconnaissance are marvelously informative and we have built much of the last two months of detailed work upon them. We suffer for want of the same kind of magnetic data. Eventually the records we are collecting now may show us the stripes, but we cannot compare what we are doing on the two ships while we are still at sea. Moreover, we are looking for rather small anomalies in a total earth's magnetic field which has a steep gradient in this region. This is comparable with looking for irregular teeth on a sloping saw blade, and it is difficult to compare the records until the slope is removed by computer. All this we knew before we sailed but we did not expect to be making our first magnetic reconnaissance when the expedition was almost ready to leave Melanesia.

Lacking any present knowledge of magnetic stripes, we are driven back on the other weapons in our armory, chief of which for this purpose is topography. We have learned a great deal related to crustal movement in Melanesia. The most common effect of convection in the mantle is the elevation of the overlying crust. This produces plateaus on land and midocean ridges in ocean basins. When we planned the expedition, one of the explanations for the shallow depths of Melanesia was that they marked a supposed Melanesian Rise formed by a mantle bulge. It was thought to trend under the Lord Howe Rise and the Fiji Plateau with a fracture zone offset between the two parts. This has proved to be only partially correct. The Fiji Plateau is shallow because of a mantle bulge, although it is a peculiar one. The Lord Howe Rise is entirely different, being not an elevated fragment of oceanic crust but a sunken fragment of an ancient continent, Melantis. If spreading has occurred, the high continents and continental fragments have moved apart, and thus the centers of spreading are to be sought under the deep basins. The Tasman and New Caledonia basins should be regarded as the equivalents of the continental crack along the Red Sea. This is a suggestion that I heard several times when I visited New Zealand and Australia before the expedition. It shows the difference in thinking of continental and marine geologists. A land geologist tends to think of an oceanic deep as an anomalous crack between shallow ridges, whereas a marine geologist considers a shallow ridge as an anomalous elevation between normal deeps. In Melanesia both views are partially correct.

The land geologists looked upon the Tasman Sea and New Caledonia basins as former centers of spreading because many puzzling features of the geology of Australia and New Zealand can be explained if they were once closed. For example, the apparent source region for some sediments is separated from the region of deposition by the New Caledonia Basin. We found no new evidence bearing directly on this question, although our magnetic observations may eventually provide a test. However, the two new fracture zones tell us something closely related which has a bearing on the spreading of other parts of Melanesia. The zones are the linear topography resulting from movement of crustal blocks on opposite sides of very long faults. They indicate the direction of movement. Compare the very different topography and structures that would be expected if the South Fiji Basin, for example, was formed by sea floor spreading north-south or alternatively east-west. If the spreading was north and south from a mid-basin line trending east-west, the margins of spreading crust would move past the immobile crust on the east and west sides and form north-south fracture zones. Any continental blocks in the area would be split along east-west lines and moved either north or south, any trenches formed by down-buckles of the crust would be at the northern and southern margins of the basin. This is quite unlike the existing features. Instead east-west spreading is suggested by the existence of fracture zone boundaries to north and south, by bordering continental blocks oriented north-south, and by a trench on the eastern side. All this may be coincidence, but the Cook fracture zone seems to confirm it. The zone is in the right position to be the boundary between parts of the sea floor which have spread east-west at different rates. Moreover, it appears to extend across the waist of the Africa-shaped basin as the d'Entrecasteau fracture zone does across the eastern Coral Sea Basin.

We can now perceive a possible pattern of mantle convection and crustal drift in Melanesia which is different from what occurs elsewhere. The Fiji Plateau, high and hot and sitting over a great mound of the mantle, resembles the scum over a convection cell in a pot of cocoa rather than part of a great linear upwelling like that under the midocean mountain system. Some horizontal movement is suggested by earthquakes, cracks, and rifts in the crust west of Fiji, and by tear faults and trenches around the borders of the plateau. However, the tear faults—the Vityaz Trench and the Hunter fracture zone—are largely inactive and may be much older features than the plateau. This plateau may be the result of an upward boil of the hot mantle which has adjusted itself within much older boundaries. Being so extraordinarily hot and otherwise peculiar, it may be in a short-lived, transient stage of convection which is not present elsewhere on earth at the moment. It may be just starting to spread for the first time, or equally possibly, be about to spread where it has spread before.

The other part of the pattern is evident in the small ocean basins separating fragments of Melantis and growing island arcs. These are basins which took their present form because of the occurrence of the cocoa-pot type of small cell convection in the past. When they were spreading, they may have been high and hot like the Fiji Plateau. That was long ago because they are not active and have been deeply blanketed by slowly accumulating sediment. They may always have been deep or they may be subsided plateaus. Melanesia appears to have had an odd history compared to much of the rest of the world, but then we went there only because it is an odd place.

3 september-11 september 1967
CHAPTER THIRTEEN

# End of the Affair

**CHAPTER THIRTEEN** *Argo* and *Horizon* were well met on the great plain of the South Fiji Basin, exchanged ceremonial shots and passed on toward the next seismic station. George Shor and I had improvised a series of four seismic stations in the Kermadec Island arc and the Kermadec Trench to complete our profile of crustal structure from Australia to the deep Pacific. Originally, we had reasoned that some older measurements far to the north would serve but thought better of it as the expedition developed. However, our background information suddenly dropped back to the level of the *Capricorn* Expedition in 1952–1953 when Russ Raitt had made the northern measurements. Then we had had hardly any soundings to guide us in selecting sites for seismic stations. During *Nova* the soundings had been so numerous that most of the stations were picked well in advance of execution. But planning is required to compile the soundings and it had not been done in the Kermadec region because it was not originally one of our goals.

We managed to prepare the rudiments of an outline map of part of the first station site by mutual tracking with Radar and exchange of soundings by radio. That gave us the trend of the main ridge in which we were interested and the station was successfully completed. A novel feature was that Alan and the girls kept recording natural earthquakes which inter-

**219**

fered with the accurately timed artificial explosions. The New Zealand Navy has found a field of active submarine volcanoes in this region which keep rumbling and shaking, and we assumed we were recording them. The shallow ridge had a thick crust like the Lord Howe Rise and Norfolk Ridge and consequently we had a very long shooting run and an equal time listening. An expedition leg must sometime end and the free time beyond the minimum to steam to port gradually decreases. Several of these very long stations would require more time than we had remaining.

The next day we were supposed to be shooting along a basin between the Colville and Kermadec ridges but the effort was ill-starred. Up and down went the mountainous sea floor and round and about went the echoes of the explosions, creating confusingly timed records. Remembering that time takes the measure of all the world George Shor called us to a halt and limited his objective to a modest determination of the structure of the upper crustal layers. While we were sitting and receiving shots, Al Price, the second mate, observed the rise of a very curious puff of black cloud or smoke from the horizon to the northwest. He thought it might be from one of the sometimes-active volcanoes of the area and we were very excited. We kept a constant watch on the spot until it was obscured by showers. Sure enough, several more black puffs appeared. Either a volcano was erupting or we were being victimized by some very peculiar cloud formations. I radioed Shor, who observed the same phenomenon from *Horizon*, and we had a visible triangulation giving a distance of less than ten miles. At that range, a volcanic eruption would be swamping the seismic recordings and probably would be pretty deafening even to sailors. Perhaps a meteorologist would have become more interested at the thought of those peculiar clouds, but we all felt rather deflated.

The third seismic station in this group was shot for sixty miles along the unknown crest of the Kermadec Ridge. It can be described briefly as a harrowing but successful effort midst mist and rain and the threat of 30-knot winds changing into gales. By early afternoon we were done, having started sixteen hours before, and went off to the Kermadec Trench for the last station. This is one of the least-known of the great trenches that are more than five miles deep and we knew far less about it than we would have if we had expected to work there. The countdown of hours to port was still favorable so we had time for a modest survey to locate the station in the axis of the trench. Shor and I established a Mason-Dixon line, north of which was their territory and south of which was ours, and we set a rendezvous point for 0800 the next morning at the position of the trench suggested by a Russian survey some years before. Waving to each other we parted and since each could clearly see the other, we absentmindedly assumed that we were at the same point. Indeed, we incontrovertibly were at the same point relative to each other and in geographical coordinates. Perhaps it was excusable that no one remembered to find out where the other ship *thought* it was—which is not the same thing—but from this small lapse came a rude awakening.

At least, I think it a rude awakening to climb out of bed at 0600 hours, pour down half a cup of aging coffee, walk to the bridge to find that the dead-reckoning position is in doubt by ten miles, walk to the laboratory and learn that the depth is almost a mile shallower than expected, and radio *Horizon* to learn that according to their dead reckoning the ships should be almost side by side. Near us they were not because they were in very different depths and could not be detected on our Radar, which has a range of twenty miles. I had an uneasy feeling of having experienced this before. I wondered if psychology was keeping up with the times and a pithy French phrase was available for recurring events that are sensed by Radar and echo sounder—*déjà électronique* perhaps?

In order to receive an answer it is necessary to ask a question and somehow we were not asking the right one. Were the ships now out of touch because they would have thought they were out of touch if we had each been invisible when last we saw each other? An awkward question but it was one of many posed during an awkward hour. I radioed *Horizon* to ask where it had been when we were last side by side. (Navigators get nervous if you ask them where they *thought* they had been.) A long pause followed during which the watch

officer on *Horizon* presumably reasoned, "Doesn't he know
where we were when we were side by side? Is he accusing us
of something?" The radioed position showed that, as we waved
at each other, the navigators on the two ships had differed by
about twenty miles in their opinions of our position, we believing a northern position and they a southern. If neither ship had
made any mistakes since then, *Horizon* was north of us and
the two ships were briskly proceeding away from each other
at cruising speed. The ships reversed course and somewhere
in the mist and rain squall that frustrated our Radar, we hoped
that we were headed toward each other for a rendezvous. The
logic on which the course reversal was based was more than
I could explain when none of us had had any breakfast, so I
went off to have some. In the mess hall I began to wonder if
I could understand it myself or if we were lost in a trackless
sea. Fortunately, Sean Solomon came by with his fried eggs.
I had discovered a few days before that a quarter of a century
apart we had attended the same college and even lived in the
same student house, and thus by all the laws of boola-boola,
he seemed a sensible choice to check a problem in relativistic
navigation before breakfast. While his eggs grew cold, he did
so and I felt more confident by the time my eggs arrived and
became only slightly cooled. The problem is in essence this:
two submarines unknown to each other are side by side but
only their radio antennas are out of the water. One says "I am
at the equator"; and the other says, "I am twenty miles south
of the equator." They state that they are at the same longitude.
They decide to each sail 100 miles east and then the one on
the equator will sail south ten miles, and the one south of the
equator will sail north ten miles and they will then surface and
be at the same spot. If they attempt to do this, since they were
in fact together at the start, they will be twenty miles apart at
the end and the one that thought it was south will end up
north.

A faint then steadying pip on the Radar screen showed
all was well and at last the ships could again see each other.
The problem arose that *Horizon* was in water half a mile
deeper than we were, but that merely meant she had found
the axis of the trench. The last seismic station of *Nova* could

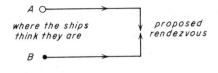

**Why we had trouble rendez-vousing over the Kermadec Trench.**

begin. When I left the bridge and went to the fantail, I found a huddle of six people in bright yellow slickers with the pointed helmets up. They looked for all the world like a meeting of an oriental Ku Klux Klan and I wondered if I should get the copy of quotations from Chairman Mao which I had prudently purchased in Brisbane. They turned out to be Alan and Helen and Duffy and other familiar faces preparing to launch hydrophones to listen for the next six hours.

This seems a good time to consider the problem of ending this personal journal of the *Nova* Expedition. If I remember my college reading, Aldous Huxley said in *Chrome Yellow* that it takes two men to finish a picture, one to paint it and one to shoot him so he will stop. Normally, books about exploration end with the author safely at home. However, this is at least intended to be a book about exploring ideas with some sailing around for local color. One of the main attractions of the pursuit of ideas is that it never ends anywhere and thus any geographical place may be an equally logical choice for the termination of a book about an oceanographic expedition. A less personal aftermath can record the arrival of the ships in San Diego and the last sailor home from the sea. The bookkeeping will be balanced and the computer will sum the distance sailed and the samples taken. Meanwhile, there is something to be said for ending the book on the sea where the main events occurred, are occurring, and will occur—for ending it here and now.

Where is this place? This is a spot, although casually come by, with geographical, geological, and historical interest.

It is the axis of the southern part of the great Kermadec Trench. Where we are is far from the deepest place in the trench but it is 27,862 feet down to the nearest mud. That is the deepest place so far encountered on the expedition and thus admirably suited for an upbeat ending—from now on it is all uphill to Auckland. Geologically, we have been pursuing ideas about the origin of mountains, plateaus, and movements of the crust. Below us is a vast furrow, a downbend produced by some of the greatest forces acting on the surface of the earth. Earthquakes are as abundant here as anywhere on earth and they extend down from this trench on a sloping plane 400 miles into the interior of the earth. This plane dips underground below the trench and can be traced under Fiji where I first joined this expedition. Thus, the beginning and the end are connected by the very evidence of deformation of the earth which we have been studying.

When is now? We are increasingly detached from the world. The time involved must differ but eventually everyone begins to forget old ways and adopt the new. How long has it been since I heard anyone mention a family at home? A few days, perhaps a week? Once it was a matter of hours. Somehow it seems normal to shoot a seismic station, haul in a magnetometer, log a sounding, or plan a rendezvous. Is there still an island somewhere in this endless and timeless sea? Did Captain Cook or Sir John Murray ever think that land was real after the years on the *Endeavor* or the *Challenger*? Being the men they were, I wonder what they were thinking when they, long at sea, sailed by this very spot. Very likely their minds turned to the significance and future of their work and in a more detached way to knowledge and science.

Here about two hundred years ago passed Captain Cook, seeking a southern continent in the Pacific and on his way to proving it did not exist. Through here on 12 July 1874 went the *Challenger* with John Murray on the first oceanographic expedition in the Pacific, on course from Wellington to the Kermadec Islands. By star and sun observations they found an easterly current, but they did not know that the trench existed. After ninety-three years, here we are the latest of many oceanographic expeditions in the Pacific. Science, according to Derek

Price and other students of the science of science, grows ever faster. If the *Challenger* Expedition were transported here through time—and what a navigation problem that would be —the members might care to visit our ship, which would not look so very different from theirs. But how amazed they would be after a day on board! They would find us with unknown technology and pursuing undreamed dreams. We may look to a time in the future when another expedition will come here with technology unknown to us and pursuing undreamed dreams. How long will that be? Perhaps, allowing for the growth of science, it might be as little as twenty years before the changes will be as great as between now and the *Challenger* Expedition. After all, within a very few years the number of people receiving a doctorate in oceanography each year in the United States will be equal to the total number who have received degrees until this time. Change will be rapid; will *Nova* have contributed anything to that imaginary expedition of the future which will be equivalent to what *Challenger* contributed to us?

What are the contributions and what will the changes be? First will be technology. Our stumbling efforts on *Nova* and before have helped bring about satellite navigation, stabilized ships, deep diving submersibles, cameras, televisions, probes, and sensors, which we do not yet have and which will seem so quaint twenty years from now. Second will be the problems and the location of the research front in oceanography and marine geology in particular. We have just seen, in the sea floor spreading hypothesis, an astounding culmination of a very great effort to understand the deformation of the earth. The broad principles were demonstrated just in time to influence our planning and execution of *Nova*. We have found many puzzling and previously unknown structures and anomalies during *Nova* and they will require new, more elaborate or more flexible versions of the basic hypothesis. The factors underlying the origin of features like the Fiji Plateau and Norfolk Ridge are hardly even suggested, but whatever their explanation, it will have to take into account the discoveries of *Nova*. Of course, these discoveries will go on, first in the legs of the expedition that will follow the ones described here. More important, however, will be the aggregate result of the continuing study and integration of our data with those of the past and future. Science grows rapidly because it is free. The results of *Nova* will be almost immediately available in Wellington, Sydney, and Noumea, as well as La Jolla. The samples will be available to serious scientists anywhere in the world.

When I try to judge the contributions of the *Challenger* Expedition, it seems to me that of many, perhaps the most important was the creation of a widespread feeling of wonder and excitement about the oceans among the people of Great Britain and the world. That cannot again be done with the same impact, but in this book I have tried to impart some of my own wonder and excitement about the sea with the hope that others may come to feel the same way. The second really important contribution of the *Challenger* Expedition was not samples nor books describing the samples but the training of the naturalist of the expedition, the young Sir John Murray, who wrote many of the books. Without him oceanography would be very different today. Without the voyage of the *Beagle*, what would Darwin and evolution and biology and our every thought be today? In the long run, the sparking of the first enduring enthusiasm in students and young scientists may be the most important function of any expedition. I would not surmise which one, but I hope that someone among the many on *Argo* and *Horizon* will be the leader of an expedition twenty years from now and that he, at least, in all the world, will want to inspire some students because of *Nova*.

march 1968
CHAPTER FOURTEEN

# *Aftermath*

**CHAPTER FOURTEEN** *Horizon* arrived home on 14 October after sailing 31,439 miles, and *Argo* on 19 December after 41,675 miles. For most of those distances we now have profiles of the topography, sub-bottom structure, and magnetic field. We have large numbers of samples of rock, bottom sediment, water, and air, and have vastly increased the number of measurements of heat flow and crustal structure in Melanesian waters. The data were collected to solve problems and the analysis has begun. The first short scientific paper based on expedition results was published in *Nature* on 9 December, or ten days before *Argo* reached the dock in San Diego. It discussed the correlation between heat flow and topography discovered in July on *Horizon* and the paper was written on shipboard. As anticipated, many of the major results of the expedition will be presented next month at the annual meeting of the American Geophysical Union in Washington. A whole morning session will be devoted to the marine geology and geophysics of Melanesia, and talks will be given by oceanographers from Lamont Geological Institute and the Hawaiian Institute of Geophysics as well as from Scripps. Our preparation for these meetings has required a very concentrated effort but as a result we have reached a stage of data processing which would normally have taken us at least a year. Perhaps, if there are not too many distractions, the initial analysis will all be awaiting publication in another year.

Unfortunately, once on shore it is always difficult to focus any effort on analysis that approaches the paroxysm of data collecting on a ship. Of course we do not really work only forty hours a week when ashore so it is not mere time expended that makes the difference. It is the many alternatives to working on the expedition data that exist. One problem is

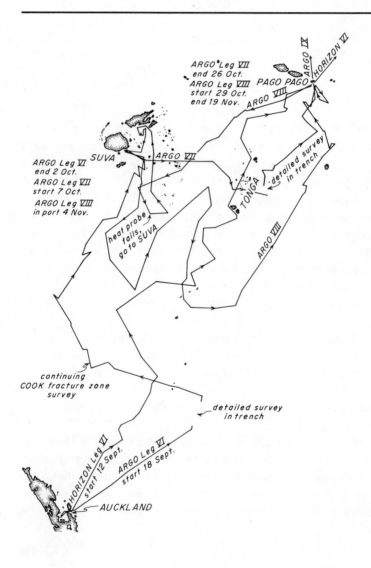

assembling the records and the people who are to work on them in the same place. Helsley is back in Texas, Biehler is in Cambridge, Winterer is on a passenger ship somewhere between Belgium and western Australia. Galehouse is back at San Francisco State College, Wilde is at Berkeley, and Aronson is at the University of California at Santa Barbara. Meanwhile at Scripps the ships keep busy. Stu Smith and Roger Larson have each led a short expedition to try to establish how the Gulf of California was formed and we are often involved in planning the next stage in this investigation. *Argo* has just departed on the first leg of a year-long round-the-world expedition called *Circe*. History again repeats itself. George Shor went on the first leg to Hawaii to solve a problem which came up a few months ago and also to test some gear. Dan Karig will board the ship at Hawaii and try to collect more data related to his thesis problem which developed during *Nova*. At this instant *Argo* is undergoing engine repairs for ten days in Hawaii. The satellite navigation system still has not been delivered—but there. is no point in starting this book over again.

An expedition is a group of people working together. Those who carried out *Nova* in the field are listed below, following the itinerary of the ships. Only a very few stayed on for the whole expedition. For two ships we had four captains and twelve chief scientists; we also had six cooks. At one time or another 178 people caught the fever called *Nova*.

# THE GENERAL SCHEDULE OF THE NOVA EXPEDITION

## ARGO

**LEG I     E. Goldberg***
17 Apr., San Diego to
16 May, Pago Pago

**LEG II     W. G. Van Dorn***
19 May, Pago Pago to
9 June, Honolulu

**LEG III     H. B. Craig***
16 June, Honolulu to
8 July, Suva

**LEG IV     E. L. Winterer***
12 July, Suva to
8 Aug., Noumea

**LEG V     H. W. Menard***
(1st half)     11 Aug., Noumea to
               23 Aug., Brisbane
(2nd half)     25 Aug., Brisbane to
               12 Sept., Auckland

**LEG VI     H. B. Craig***
18 Sept., Auckland to
2 Oct., Suva

**LEG VII     R. L. Fisher***
(1st half)     7 Oct., Suva to
               16 Oct., Tonga Islands
(2nd half)     16 Oct., Tonga Islands to
               26 Oct., Pago Pago

**LEG VIII     V. Vacquier***
(1st half)     29 Oct., Pago Pago to
               4 Nov., Suva
(2nd half)     4 Nov., Suva to
               19 Nov., Pago Pago

**LEG IX     A. E. Engle***
22 Nov., Pago Pago to
11 Dec., Hilo

**LEG X     P. Crampton***
11 Dec., Hilo to
19 Dec., San Diego

## HORIZON

**LEG I**
(1st half)     **T. Chase***
               18 Apr., Kwajalein to
               3 May, Brisbane
(2nd half)     **S. M. Smith***
               6 May, Brisbane to
               29 May, Noumea

**LEG II     E. L. Winterer***
1 June, Noumea to
1 July, Suva

**LEG III     H. W. Menard***
4 July, Suva to
11 July, Suva

**LEG IV     H. W. Menard***
13 July, Suva to
7 Aug., Noumea

**LEG V     G. G. Shor, Jr.***
(1st half)     11 Aug., Noumea to
               23 Aug., Brisbane
(2nd half)     25 Aug., Brisbane to
               12 Sept., Auckland

**LEG VI     D. E. Karig***
(1st half)     12 Sept., Auckland to
               26 Sept., Pago Pago
(2nd half)     26 Sept., Pago Pago to
               14 Oct., San Diego

* Scientist in charge (SIC)

## PARTICIPANTS IN NOVA EXPEDITION

| | | ARGO | | | | | | | | | | HORIZON | | | | | |
|---|---|---|---|---|---|---|---|---|---|---|---|---|---|---|---|---|---|
| LEG. NO. | | 1 | 2 | 3 | 4 | 5 | 6 | 7 | 8 | 9 | 10 | 1 | 2 | 3 | 4 | 5 | 6 |
| **Abranson, Christian-Erik**<br>Student | | | | | | | | | | | | | | ▦ | ▦ | ▦ | |
| **Acton, William**<br>Seaman | | ▦ | ▦ | ▦ | | | | | | | | | | | | | |
| **Allison, E. C.**<br>Professor, San Diego<br>State College | | | | | | | | | | | | | | ▦ | | | |
| **Anceaux, Johannes T.**<br>Visiting professor,<br>Univ. California, San Diego,<br>from Belgium | | ▦ | | | | | | | | | | | | | | ▦ | |
| **Aronson, James**<br>Geologist　　　**Ashore** | | | | | | | | | | | | | | | | | |
| **Aronson, Arlene**<br>Geologist　　　**Ashore** | | | | | | | | | | | | | | | | | |
| **Arsenault, Albert**<br>Mate | | | | | | | | | | | | ▦ | ▦ | ▦ | ▦ | ▦ | |
| **Avery, Glenn J.**<br>Oiler | | | | | | ▦ | ▦ | ▦ | ▦ | ▦ | | | | | | | |
| **Baker, Bruce**<br>Physician | | | | | | | | | | | | | ▦ | ▦ | ▦ | | |
| **Bell III, Miller L.**<br>Undergraduate,<br>Univ. California, San Diego | | | | ▦ | ▦ | | | | | | | | | | | | |
| **Berger, Jonathon**<br>Student　　　**Ashore** | | | | | | | | | | | | | | | | | |
| **Biehler, S.**<br>Professor, MIT | | | | | ▦ | | | | | | | | | | | | |
| **Bieri, Rudolph H.**<br>Physicist | | ▦ | | | | | | | | | | | | | | | |
| **Block, Barry**<br>Professor　　　**Ashore** | | | | | | | | | | | | | | | | | |
| **Bonham, John W.**<br>Mate | | | | | | | | | | | | | | | ▦ | ▦ | ▦ |
| **Brennen, Robert E.**<br>Technician | | ▦ | ▦ | ▦ | | | | | | | | | | | | | |
| **Briggs, Robert A.**<br>Engineer | | ▦ | ▦ | ▦ | ▦ | ▦ | | | | | | | | | | | |

| | | ARGO | | | | | | | | | | HORIZON | | | | | |
|---|---|---|---|---|---|---|---|---|---|---|---|---|---|---|---|---|---|
| LEG NO. | 1 | 2 | 3 | 4 | 5 | 6 | 7 | 8 | 9 | 10 | 1 | 2 | 3 | 4 | 5 | 6 |
| **Bristol, Wayne E.** Mate | | | | | | | | | | | ▓ | ▓ | | | | |
| **Brown, William I.** Engineer | | | ▓ | ▓ | ▓ | ▓ | ▓ | | | | | | | | | |
| **Buchser, Robert** Oiler | | | | | | ▓ | ▓ | ▓ | ▓ | | | | | | | |
| **Bullard, Edward C.** Professor, Cambridge Univ. and Scripps Inst. Oceanography | | | | | | | | | | | | | ▓ | ▓ | | |
| **Carcogno, Ross C.** Oiler | | | | | | | | | | | ▓ | | | | | |
| **Carter, A.** Geologist, Univ. New South Wales, Australia | | | | | | | | | | | | ▓ | | | | |
| **Chandler, Daniel F.** Seaman | | | | ▓ | ▓ | ▓ | ▓ | ▓ | ▓ | ▓ | | | | | | |
| **Chase, Clement G.** Student | | | | | | | | | | | | | ▓ | ▓ | ▓ | |
| **Chase, Thomas E.** Geological Specialist | | | | | | | | | | | ▓ | | | | | |
| **Chavarria, Carlos A.** Seaman | | | | | | | ▓ | | | | | | | | | |
| **Christensen, Robert** Seaman | ▓ | ▓ | ▓ | | | | | | | | | | | | | |
| **Chung, Yu-Chia** Student | | ▓ | | | | | | | | | | | | | | |
| **Church, Thomas M.** Student | ▓ | | | | | | | | | | | | | | | |
| **Ciccarelli, Virgil** Physician | | | ▓ | ▓ | | | | | | | | | | | | |
| **Ciganero, Leonard P.** Radioman | | | | | | | | | | | ▓ | ▓ | ▓ | ▓ | ▓ | ▓ |
| **Clarke, Robert G.** Engineer | | | | | | | | | | | | | | | | ▓ |
| **Clay, Amos** Electrician | | | | ▓ | ▓ | ▓ | | | | | | | | | | |
| **Colaw, Victor M.** Seaman | | | | | | | | | | | ▓ | ▓ | ▓ | ▓ | ▓ | ▓ |

| | | ARGO | | | | | | | | | | HORIZON | | | | | |
|---|---|---|---|---|---|---|---|---|---|---|---|---|---|---|---|---|---|
| LEG NO. | 1 | 2 | 3 | 4 | 5 | 6 | 7 | 8 | 9 | 10 | 1 | 2 | 3 | 4 | 5 | 6 |
| **Coleman, Garrett S.** Mate | | | | ▓ | ▓ | ▓ | ▓ | ▓ | ▓ | ▓ | | | | | | |
| **Conolly, John R.** Geologist, Univ. Sydney, Australia | | | | | | | | | | | ▓ | | | | | |
| **Cooper, George** Cook | | | | | | | | ▓ | ▓ | | | | | | | |
| **Cothrum, Edward W.** Oiler | | | | | | | | | | | ▓ | ▓ | ▓ | ▓ | ▓ | ▓ |
| **Cozad, Jack** Seaman | ▓ | ▓ | ▓ | ▓ | ▓ | ▓ | ▓ | ▓ | ▓ | | | | | | | |
| **Craig, Harmon B.** Professor | | | ▓ | | ▓ | | | | | | | | | | | |
| **Craig, Valerie** Technician | | | | | ▓ | | | | | | | | | | | |
| **Crampton, Perry J.** Technician | | | | | | | | | ▓ | ▓ | | | | | | |
| **Cruz, Alfredo** Physician | | | | | ▓ | ▓ | | | | | | | | | | |
| **Cunningham, Lyle M.** Radioman | | | | | | | | | | | | | | ▓ | ▓ | ▓ |
| **Currey, Robert J.** Cook | | | | | | | | | | | | | | ▓ | ▓ | |
| **Dahlberg, William I.** Engineer | | | | | | | | | | | | | | ▓ | ▓ | |
| **Davis, Bertram E.** Engineer | | | | | | | | ▓ | ▓ | | | | | | | |
| **Davis, Lawrence E.** Captain | ▓ | ▓ | ▓ | ▓ | | | | | | | | | | | | |
| **Dixon, Frederick S.** Marine technician | | | ▓ | ▓ | ▓ | ▓ | ▓ | ▓ | ▓ | | | | | | | |
| **Dubois, J.** Geophysicist, ORSTOM, New Caledonia | | | | | | | ▓ | | | | | ▓ | | | | |
| **Earl, John L.** Technician | ▓ | | | | | | | | | | | | | | | |
| **Edmonson, David B.** Student | | | | | ▓ | | | | | | | | | | | |
| **Engel, Albert E.** Professor | | | | | | | | | ▓ | | | | | | | |

| LEG NO. | ARGO | | | | | | | | | | HORIZON | | | | | |
|---|---|---|---|---|---|---|---|---|---|---|---|---|---|---|---|---|
| | 1 | 2 | 3 | 4 | 5 | 6 | 7 | 8 | 9 | 10 | 1 | 2 | 3 | 4 | 5 | 6 |
| **Evans, Clyde** — Cook | | | | | | | ■ | | | | ■ | | | | | |
| **Ferris, Noel L.** — Captain | | | | | | | | | | | ■ | | | | | |
| **Fisher, Robert L.** — Geologist | | | | | | | ■ | | | | | | | | | |
| **Francheteau, Jean M.** — Student | | | ■ | ■ | ■ | | | | | | | | | | | ■ |
| **Frase, Jr., Charles A.** — Cook | | | | | | | | | | | ■ | ■ | ■ | ■ | | |
| **Fruchter, J. S.** — Student | | ■ | | | | | | | | | | | | | | |
| **Fuller, Jr., Robert W.** — Electrician | ■ | ■ | | | | | | ■ | ■ | | | | | | | |
| **Fullerton, Donald L.** — Oiler | | | | | | | | | | | ■ | ■ | ■ | | | |
| **Galehouse, Jon** — Post-doctoral fellow | | | | | | | | | | | | ■ | | | | |
| **Gall, George T.** — Engineer | ■ | ■ | ■ | ■ | | | | | | | | | | | | |
| **Garner, Larkin O.** — Seaman | ■ | ■ | ■ | ■ | ■ | ■ | ■ | ■ | ■ | | | | | | | |
| **Gobble, Thomas** — Physician | ■ | | | | | | | | | | | | | | ■ | |
| **Goldberg, Edward D.** — Professor | ■ | | | | | | | | | | | | | | | |
| **Greenhouse, John P.** — Student | | | | | | | | | | | | | | ■ | ■ | |
| **Groueff, Stephane** — Reporter from *Paris-Match* | | | | | | | ■ | | | | | | | | | |
| **Hansen, Terry** — Captain | | | | | | | | | | | | | | ■ | ■ | ■ |
| **Hardy, John A.** — Technician | | | | | | ■ | ■ | | | | | | | | | |
| **Harless, James G.** — Oiler | ■ | ■ | ■ | ■ | | | | | | | | | | | | |
| **Helsley, Charles E.** — Geophysicist, Grad. Res. Center Southwest | | | ■ | | | | | | | | | | | | | |

| | | ARGO | | | | | | | | | | | HORIZON | | | | | |
|---|---|---|---|---|---|---|---|---|---|---|---|---|---|---|---|---|---|---|
| LEG NO. | | 1 | 2 | 3 | 4 | 5 | 6 | 7 | 8 | 9 | 10 | | 1 | 2 | 3 | 4 | 5 | 6 |
| **Herrera, R. G.** Geologist, British Petroleum Co., Australia | | | | | | | | | | | | | | ■ | | | | |
| **Hilde, Thomas W.** Geological specialist | | | | | | | | ■ | | | | | | | | | | |
| **Hohnhaus, George W.** Marine technician | | | | | | | | | | | | | | | ■ | ■ | | |
| **Holden, John C.** Student, Univ. California, Berkeley | | ■ | | ■ | | | | | | | | | | ■ | | | | |
| **Hom, Beatrice** Technician | | | | | | | | | | | ■ | | | | | | | |
| **Horwatt, Edward A.** Engineer | | ■ | ■ | ■ | | | | | | | | | | | | | | |
| **Huggett, Robert J.** Student | | | | ■ | ■ | | | | | | | | | | | | | |
| **Hughes, Wallace** Oiler | | | | | ■ | | | | | | | | | | | | | |
| **Isezaki, N.** Student, Tokyo Univ. | | | | | | | | ■ | ■ | | | | | | | | | |
| **Jacobs, William F.** Engineer | | | | | | | | | | | | | | ■ | ■ | ■ | | |
| **Jinks, Robert C.** Oiler | | ■ | | | | | | | | | | | | | | | | |
| **Johnson, David A.** Student | | | | | | | | | | | | | | | | ■ | ■ | |
| **Jones, Alan C.** Engineer | | | ■ | | | ■ | | | | | | | | | | | | |
| **Karig, Daniel** Student | | | | | | ■ | | | | | | | | | | | | ■ |
| **Kesler, George W.** Engineer | | ■ | ■ | ■ | ■ | ■ | ■ | ■ | ■ | ■ | ■ | | | | | | | |
| **Kidd, William L.** Engineer | | ■ | ■ | ■ | | | | | | | | | | | | | | |
| **Kinney, Ernest K.** Seaman | | | | | | | | | | | | | | ■ | ■ | ■ | ■ | |
| **Kinsfather, John O.** Student | | | | ■ | ■ | | | | | | | | | | | | ■ | |
| **Kirk, Helen K.** Geophysical specialist | | | | | | ■ | | | | | | | | | | | | ■ |

| | ARGO | | | | | | | | | | HORIZON | | | | | |
|---|---|---|---|---|---|---|---|---|---|---|---|---|---|---|---|---|
| LEG NO. | 1 | 2 | 3 | 4 | 5 | 6 | 7 | 8 | 9 | 10 | 1 | 2 | 3 | 4 | 5 | 6 |
| **Koide, Minoru** Chemical specialist | █ | | | | | | | | | | | | | | | |
| **Kolhage, James M.** Technician | █ | █ | | | | | | | | | | | | | | |
| **Kuykendoll, James E.** Electronics technician | | | | | | | | | | | █ | | | | | |
| **Launay, Jean** Geologist, ORSTOM, New Caledonia | | | | | | | | | | | █ | | | | | |
| **Larson, Roger L.** Student | | | | | | | | | | | | █ | | █ | | |
| **Long, Ernest E.** Oiler | | | | █ | | | | | | | | | | | | |
| **Magnussen, C. M.** Seaman | █ | █ | █ | █ | █ | █ | █ | █ | █ | | | | | | | |
| **Maricich, John** Engineer | █ | █ | █ | █ | █ | █ | | | | | | | | | | |
| **McGowan, Delpha D.** Technician | | | | █ | | | | | | | | | | | | █ |
| **Menard, Andrew** Undergraduate, Antioch College | | | | | | | █ | | █ | | | | | | | |
| **Menard, H. W.** Professor | | | | █ | | | | | | | | | █ | | | |
| **Meyer, Charles** Student | | | | | | | | █ | | | | | | | | |
| **Mogi, A.** Geologist, Japan Marine Safety Agency | | | | | | | █ | | | | | | | | | |
| **Mulligan, Michael** Seaman | | | █ | █ | █ | | | | | | | | | | | |
| **Nadolski, Paul J.** Oiler | | | | | | | █ | █ | | | █ | | | | | |
| **Nagasaka, K.** Geophysicist, Japan Meteorological Agency | | | | | | | █ | █ | | | | | | | | |
| **Newhouse, Dale A.** Technician | | | | █ | █ | | | | | | | | | | | █ |
| **Nicholson, James J.** Student | | | | █ | █ | | | | | | | | | | | |

| | ARGO | | | | | | | | | | HORIZON | | | | | |
| LEG NO. | 1 | 2 | 3 | 4 | 5 | 6 | 7 | 8 | 9 | 10 | 1 | 2 | 3 | 4 | 5 | 6 |
|---|---|---|---|---|---|---|---|---|---|---|---|---|---|---|---|---|
| **Nierenberg, William A.**<br>Director,<br>Scripps Inst. Oceanography | | | | | | | X | | | | | | | | | |
| **Normark, William R.**<br>Student | | | | | | | | | | | X | | | | | |
| **Oboler, Steven**<br>Undergraduate, Antioch College | X | X | X | | | | | | | | | | | | | |
| **Ohlund, Evan S.**<br>Oiler | X | | | | X | X | X | X | X | | | | | | | |
| **O'Grady, Harry**<br>Engineer | | | | | | | | | | | | X | X | X | X | X |
| **Oster, Richard**<br>Electrician | | | | | | | | | | | | X | | | | |
| **Over, Stuart B.**<br>Physician | X | | | | | | | | | | | | | | | |
| **Pence, Richard H.**<br>Radioman | X | | | | | | | | | | | | | | | |
| **Peterson, Michael R.**<br>Student | | | | X | | | | | | | | | | | | |
| **Petrequin, Jean**<br>Cook | X | X | X | | | | | | | | | | | | | |
| **Phinney, Alan W.**<br>Captain | | | | | X | X | X | X | X | | | | | | | |
| **Pine, James S.**<br>Technician | | X | | | X | | | | | | | | | | | |
| **Post, Merle A.**<br>Electrician | | | | X | X | X | X | X | X | | | | | | | |
| **Price, Thomas A.**<br>Mate | X | X | X | X | X | X | X | X | X | | | | | | | |
| **Prichard, Paul**<br>Oiler | | | | | | | | | | | | | | X | X | X |
| **Probst, Richard W.**<br>Seaman | X | X | X | X | X | X | X | X | X | | | | | | | |
| **Provost, Donald**<br>Seaman | | | | X | X | X | X | X | X | | | | | | | |
| **Puech, Jean L.**<br>Geologist, ORSTOM,<br>New Caledonia | | | | | | X | | | | | X | | | | | |

| | | ARGO | | | | | | | | | | HORIZON | | | | | |
|---|---|---|---|---|---|---|---|---|---|---|---|---|---|---|---|---|---|
| LEG NO. | | 1 | 2 | 3 | 4 | 5 | 6 | 7 | 8 | 9 | 10 | 1 | 2 | 3 | 4 | 5 | 6 |
| **Quigg, Ronald N.** Seaman | | | | | | | | | | | | ■ | ■ | ■ | ■ | ■ | ■ |
| **Renner, Patricia A.** Technician | | | | | | | | | | ■ | | | | | | | |
| **Richardson, Monroe I.** Mechanic | | | | | | | | ■ | ■ | | | | | | | | |
| **Riley, Peter J.** Seaman | | ■ | | | | | | | | | | | | | | | |
| **Robbins, Robert W.** Radioman | | | | | ■ | ■ | ■ | ■ | | | | | | | | | |
| **Rojas, Joseph** Mate | | | | | ■ | ■ | ■ | ■ | ■ | | | | | | | | |
| **Rowe, Raymond** Technician | | ■ | ■ | ■ | ■ | ■ | ■ | ■ | | | | | | | | | |
| **Sammuli, Harold** Electronics technician | | | | | | | | | | | | ■ | ■ | | | ■ | ■ |
| **Sanders, Stephen** Technician | | | | | | | | | | | | | | ■ | ■ | ■ | ■ |
| **Scarborough, Chris A.** Oiler | | ■ | ■ | ■ | ■ | ■ | ■ | ■ | ■ | | | | | | | | |
| **Schneider, Jr., T. L.** Radioman | | | | | | | | | | | | ■ | | | | | |
| **Schoenbechler, Maxine** Technician | | | | | | | | | | ■ | | | | | | | |
| **Sclater, John G.** Geophysicist | | | | ■ | | | | ■ | | | | | | | ■ | | |
| **Shipp, Jr., Richard P.** Seaman | | ■ | ■ | ■ | | | | | | | | | | | | | |
| **Shor, Jr., George G.** Geophysicist | | ■ | | | | | | | | | | | | | | ■ | |
| **Slater, Richard** Student, Univ. Sydney, Australia | | | | | | | | | | | | | | | ■ | | |
| **Slawson, Hugh P.** Student | | | | ■ | | | | | | | | | | | | | |
| **Smith, Edward** Seaman | | | | | | | | | | | | ■ | ■ | ■ | ■ | ■ | |
| **Smith, Stuart M.** Geological specialist | | | | | | | | | | | | ■ | | | | | |

| | ARGO | | | | | | | | | | HORIZON | | | | | |
|---|:-:|:-:|:-:|:-:|:-:|:-:|:-:|:-:|:-:|:-:|:-:|:-:|:-:|:-:|:-:|:-:|
| **LEG NO.** | 1 | 2 | 3 | 4 | 5 | 6 | 7 | 8 | 9 | 10 | 1 | 2 | 3 | 4 | 5 | 6 |
| **Smith, Warren** <br> Technician | | | | | █ | █ | | | █ | █ | | | █ | █ | | |
| **Solomon, Sean** <br> Student, M.I.T. | | | | | █ | █ | | | | | | | | | | |
| **Somayajulu, Bhamidipati L.** <br> Post-doctoral fellow | | | █ | | | | | | | | | | | | | |
| **Summerhayes, Colin** <br> Geologist, Dept. Sci. Ind. Res., <br> New Zealand | | | | | | █ | | | | | | | | | | |
| **Tait, Robert J.** <br> Student | | | █ | | | | | | | | | | | █ | | |
| **Taylor, Graham** <br> Student, Univ. New South Wales, <br> Australia | | | | | █ | | | | | | | | | | | |
| **Taylor, Isabel** <br> Technician | | | | | | | | | | █ | | | | | | |
| **Teixeira, Manuel M.** <br> Seaman | █ | █ | █ | █ | █ | █ | █ | █ | █ | █ | | | | | | |
| **Thomas, Baron E.** <br> Technician | | | | | | | | █ | █ | | | | | █ | █ | █ |
| **Tibbits, James G.** <br> Radioman | █ | █ | █ | █ | █ | █ | █ | █ | █ | █ | | | | | | |
| **Tobey, Wilson E.** <br> Electrician | █ | █ | █ | | | | | | | | | | | | | |
| **Toney, James B.** <br> Technician, <br> Grad. Res. Center Southwest | | | | █ | | | | | | | | | | | | |
| **Trease, Gene M.** <br> Engineer | | | | | | | | █ | █ | | | | | | | |
| **Utashiro, S.** <br> Geophysicist, <br> Japan Marine Safety Agency | | | | | | | █ | | | | | | | | | |
| **Vacquier, Victor** <br> Professor | | | | | | | █ | | | | | | | | █ | |
| **Van Der Linden, Willem** <br> Geologist, Dept. Sci. Ind. Res., <br> New Zealand | | | | | | | | | | | | | | | | |
| **Vincent, Julian** <br> Oiler | | | | | █ | █ | █ | █ | | | | | | | | |

| LEG NO. | ARGO | | | | | | | | | | HORIZON | | | | | |
|---|---|---|---|---|---|---|---|---|---|---|---|---|---|---|---|---|
| | 1 | 2 | 3 | 4 | 5 | 6 | 7 | 8 | 9 | 10 | 1 | 2 | 3 | 4 | 5 | 6 |
| **Walsh, Thomas J.** Technician | | | | | | | ▓ | | | | | | | | | |
| **Waterman, Lee S.** Laboratory technician | ▓ | ▓ | ▓ | ▓ | | | | | | | | | | | | |
| **Wyat, Carl D.** Engineer | ▓ | ▓ | ▓ | ▓ | ▓ | ▓ | ▓ | ▓ | ▓ | | | | | | | |
| **Webb, Jack A.** Seaman | ▓ | ▓ | | | | | | | | | | | | | | |
| **Weeks, William A.** Seaman | | | | | | ▓ | ▓ | ▓ | | | | | | | | |
| **Weiss, Ray F.** Student | | | ▓ | | ▓ | | | | | | | | | | | |
| **Wilde, Pat** Professor, Univ. California, Berkeley | | | | ▓ | | | | | | | | ▓ | ▓ | | | |
| **Williams, Grady N.** Cook | | | | ▓ | ▓ | ▓ | ▓ | ▓ | ▓ | | | | | | | |
| **Winterer, Edward L.** Professor | | | | ▓ | | | | | | | | | ▓ | | | |
| **Wright, Jack W.** Cook | ▓ | ▓ | ▓ | | | | | | | | | | | | | |
| **Yasui, M.** Oceanographer, Japan Meteorological Agency | | | | | | | ▓ | | | | | | | | | |
| **Yoshino, T.** Student, Tokyo Univ. | | | | | | | ▓ | | | | | | | | | |

# References and Notes

# REFERENCES AND NOTES

## CHAPTER 1

1. The cost of Cook's first voyage. J. C. Beaglehole (ed.), **The Voyage of the Endeavour,** Cambridge University Press, Cambridge, 1955.

2. The value of money in 1768. G. M. Trevelyan, **Illustrated English Social History,** vol. 3, Longmans, Green & Co., Ltd., London, 1949. Professor Seymour Harris kindly verified my inflation factor.

3. Banks' fortune. J. C. Beaglehole (ed.), **The Endeavour Journal of Joseph Banks,** Angus and Robertson, Sydney, 1962.

4. Cost of the United States Exploring Expedition. M. E. Cooley, in **Proceedings of the American Philosophical Society,** vol. 82, no. 5, 1940.

5. Outfitting *Challenger.* C. Wyville Thomson, **The Voyage of the Challenger,** Macmillan & Co., Ltd., London, 1877.

## CHAPTER 2

1. The Polynesians and errors in longitude. A. Sharp, **Ancient Voyagers in Polynesia,** University of California Press, Berkeley, 1964. In this and his earlier books Professor Sharp shows what can be done to reduce 300 years of confusing "scholarship" to an understandable and brief whole by applying critical insight and modern methods.

2. The European explorers and a quotation from La Perouse. J. N. Baker, **A History of Geographical Discovery and Exploration,** George G. Harrap & Co., Ltd., London, 1931. I have had this book with me on voyages since 1944 to see when I cross an explorer's track.

## CHAPTER 3

1. Darwin's life, and quotations from Henslow and Stokes. F. Darwin (ed.), **The Life and Letters of Charles Darwin,** vol. 1, D. Appleton & Co., Inc., New York, 1897.

2. The origin of coral reefs. Charles Darwin, **The Structure and Distribution of Coral Reefs,** University of California Press, Berkeley, 1962 paperback edition.

3. The life of Maury. F. L. Williams, **Matthew Fontaine Maury Scientist of the Sea,** Rutgers University Press, New Brunswick, 1963.

4. Drillings of Funafuti. W. J. Sollas, et al., **Report of the Coral Reef Committee,** The Royal Society, London, 1904. See also Mrs. Edgeworth Davis, **Funafuti, or Three Months on a Coral Island: An Unscientific Account of a Scientific Expedition,** Sir Isaac Pitman & Sons, Ltd., London, 1904.

## CHAPTER 4

1. Geological time scale. Geologists worked out a relative time scale during the nineteenth century which made it possible to say that one

fossil or group of fossils was older than another. For convenience they named various intervals in this relative geological time scale. Not until isotopic geochemistry was developed in the last few decades was it possible to attach an age in years to a few of the named parts of the geological time scales, and some uncertainties remain. The names and assumed ages of the last few percent of geological time are as follows in millions of years:

|  | Duration | Elapsed |
|---|---|---|
| Recent | Now | |
| | | 0 |
| Pleistocene | 1 | |
| | | 1 |
| Pliocene | 10 | |
| | | 11 |
| Miocene | 14 | |
| | | 25 |
| Oligocene | 15 | |
| | | 40 |
| Eocene | 20 | |
| | | 60 |
| Paleocene | 10 | |
| | | $70 \pm 2$ |
| Cretaceous | 65 | |
| | | $135 \pm 5$ |

2. Continental drift. A. Wegener, **Origin of Continents and Oceans,** E. P. Dutton & Co., Inc., New York, 1924.

3. Objectives and problems of marine geology. W. Bascom, **A Hole in the Bottom of the Sea,** Weidenfeld and Nicolson, London, 1961. An account of the Mohole Project and its aims.

4. H. W. Menard, **Marine Geology of the Pacific,** McGraw-Hill Book Company, New York, 1964.

5. Sea floor spreading. Numerous brief papers are in **Science, Nature,** and the **Journal of Geophysical Research** for late 1966 and 1967 and doubtless will continue.

### CHAPTER 5

1. Quote from Banks' **Endeavour Journal.** Op. cit.

2. Quote from **Moby Dick.** Melville seems to have avoided Melanesia, perhaps because of the prevalence of cannibals. See, for example, Jack London, **South Sea Tales.**

3. The ancient role of ship's captains. C. E. Fayle, **A Short History of**

**the World's Shipping Industry,** George Allen & Unwin Ltd., London, 1933.

4. Ship life in rough weather. I was cɩ the aircraft carrier *Hancock* in a typhoon that sank three destroyers east of the Philippines. Waves occasionally broke over the flight deck. Life is more rigorous in normal weather on *Horizon*. On the other hand there are smaller ships: see Francis Chichester, **Along the Clipper Way,** Hodder & Stoughton, London, 1966, or Thor Heyerdahl, **Kon-Tiki,** Rand McNally & Company, Chicago, 1950.

## CHAPTER 7

1. Scripps' shipboard procedures. For an interesting comparison see Helen Raitt, **Exploring the Deep Pacific,** W. W. Norton & Co., Inc., 1956. She also flew to Fiji to meet a Scripps expedition.

## CHAPTER 8

1. Bligh's voyage in an open boat. G. Mackaness, **The Life of Vice-Admiral William Bligh,** Angus and Robertson, Sydney, rev. ed. 1951. A matchless fictional account is given in Charles Nordhoff and James Hall, **Men Against the Sea.**

2. Sailing directions. **Sailing Directions for the Pacific Islands,** 3 vols., U. S. Navy Oceanographic Office, Washington, include information about harbors, anchorages, and other matters of interest to mariners. The second essential guide to the serious student or even casual sailor is the **Pacific Islands Year Book,** Pacific Publ. Pty., Ltd., Sydney, which gives some history and political organization and the names of incumbent officials. Care should be taken to obtain the current edition of each of these works although the editions before the Second World War are an interesting contrast.

3. Uplifted atolls in the Loyalty Islands. W. M. Davis, **The Coral Reef Problem,** American Geographical Society, New York, 1928.

4. Pelagic oozes. D. B. Ericson and G. Wollin, **The Deep and the Past,** Alfred A. Knopf, Inc., New York, 1964.

# *Index*

# INDEX

This book was set in Cairo, printed on permanent paper by Halliday Lithograph Corporation, and bound by the Maple Press Company. The designer was Richard Paul Kluga; the drawings were done by J. & R. Technical Services, Inc. The editors were Bradford Bayne and Sally Anderson. Adam Jacobs supervised the production.